KT-464-682

Vegetarianism

ISSUES
(formerly Issues for the Nineties)

Volume 19

Editor

Craig Donnellan

Independence
Educational Publishers
Cambridge

ABERDEENSHIRE LIBRARIES

ABS 2000677

First published by Independence
PO Box 295
Cambridge CB1 3XP
England

© Craig Donnellan 1998

Copyright
This book is sold subject to the condition that it shall not,
by way of trade or otherwise, be lent, resold, hired out or otherwise
circulated in any form of binding or cover other than that in which it
is published without the publisher's prior consent.

Photocopy licence
The material in this book is protected by copyright. However, the
purchaser is free to make multiple copies of particular articles for instructional
purposes for immediate use within the purchasing institution.
Making copies of the entire book is not permitted.

British Library Cataloguing in Publication Data
Vegetarianism – (Issues Series)
I. Donnellan, Craig II. Series
613.2'62

ISBN 1 86168 068 6

Printed in Great Britain
City Print Ltd
Milton Keynes

Typeset by
Claire Boyd

Cover
The illustration on the front cover is by
The Attic Publishing Co.

613.2
m009450

CONTENTS

ERBURGH ACADEMY LIBRARY

Introduction

Vegetarianism is the nineteenth volume in the series:
Issues. The aim of this series is to offer up-to-date
information about important issues in our world.

Vegetarianism looks at the dietary and ethical aspects
of vegetarianism.

The information comes from a wide variety of sources
and includes:
Government reports and statistics
Newspaper reports and features
Magazine articles and surveys
Literature from lobby groups
and charitable organisations.

It is hoped that, as you read about the many aspects
of the issues explored in this book, you will critically
evaluate the information presented. It is important
that you decide whether you are being presented
with facts or opinions. Does the writer give a biased
or an unbiased report? If an opinion is being expressed,
do you agree with the writer?

Vegetarianism offers a useful starting-point for those
who need convenient access to information about
the many issues involved. However, it is only a
starting-point. At the back of the book is a list of
organisations which you may want to contact for
further information.

*****

The great veggie debate

Is a diet without meat really more healthy? Last week Sir Paul McCartney appealed for more people to turn vegetarian as a fitting tribute to his wife. But for many, the death of Linda McCartney from breast cancer has again fuelled the debate over the wisdom of giving up meat. Here, Liz Gill hears the arguments from two doctors.

Yes says retired GP Dr David Ryde

Dr David Ryde has been a vegetarian for 20 years and a vegan – someone who eschews all animal products – for the past 15. At the age of 69 he still swims, cycles and plays squash and is planning to open a nutrition clinic in Oxford.

When I first became a vegetarian I kept a low profile because I felt people might think it was eccentric for a doctor. But then I kept discovering others and I noticed they were all slim.

I began recommending vegetarian and vegan diets to my overweight patients and got startlingly good results, far better than from any slimming clinic.

In 1982 I had a patient whose angina was so bad he couldn't get from the car park to the surgery without having to stop and take a tablet. I suggested he started to eat the way I ate. Within a month he was walking to the surgery from his home a mile away.

Shortly afterwards he and his wife moved away to be near their daughter but she rang me a few months later to say her father was a new man. I've had six patients like that since.

I am convinced our digestive system is designed for plant eaters

---

I knew this couldn't be a fluke so I started looking into the biochemistry of it all. If you take a blood sample from someone who's had a standard affluent society meal, the serum is foggy with fat particles and the red blood cells stick together in clumps.

In a vegan the serum is translucent and red cells remain separate, which means the blood can take up more oxygen and diffuse it to the tissues better. Vegans and vegetarians also have much lower cholesterol levels.

You need much more stomach acid to digest animal protein rather than plant protein – carnivorous animals produce ten times what we do – which has implications for acid dyspepsia.

Patients with chronic indigestion have seen it clear up within a week or two of changing their diet. One woman with gall bladder problems found her pain disappeared completely after she switched. It's also been effective for patients with late onset diabetes.

People say 'Where do you get your calcium from if you don't drink milk? Where do you get your protein from if you don't eat meat?' Well where does the cow get her calcium from, or the bull? They get it from vegetation. All the big powerful animals with massive bones – the horse, the elephant, the gorilla, the rhino – are plant eaters. They also worry about iron, but too much iron means the reserves can act as free radicals which damage the cells. Cancer is more common in meat eaters, as are liver and kidney disease.

I am convinced our digestive system – from the shape and movement of our jaws to the length of our bowels – is designed for plant eaters.

Most of my four children and six grandchildren are vegetarians or vegans. My son Simon, who's a vegetarian, is 6ft 1in, as strong as an ox and just about to go to Australia to compete in the Iron Man Triathlon. The record-holder for the event, which involves swimming two miles, cycling 110 and then running a marathon, is in fact a vegan.

There are an increasing number of studies to back up our case. A study of a large group of peasants in rural China who eat an almost entirely plant-based diet showed that they live longer than we do, even without a medical service.

A report from Germany showed vegans have a fifth of the bed occupancy rates in hospitals of meat eaters, and a study of a community of 35,000 Seventh Day Adventists in California found that the vegetarians among them lived six years longer on average than the meat eaters and the vegans ten years longer.

Linda McCartney's death was very unfortunate but your diet doesn't make you immortal. Vegetarians and vegans still have to die, and they die of the same things as everyone else. But the incidence of the disease is usually much less. Women is Eastern countries, for example, have one-fifth to a tenth of the rate of breast cancer of Western women.

Vegan and vegetarian cooking is not boring – we eat wonderfully – but I know not everyone can go the whole way. But anything is better than nothing. I suggest people try switching over a period of two months or try to eat only one-fifth of the meat or fish they average now and try to keep to game, which is lower in fat.

No says Dr Paul Stillman, a GP in Crawley, West Sussex

Dr Paul Stillman, 52, has been a GP for more than 20 years, during which time he has seen many patients switch to vegetarian diets. He and his family, however, still eat meat. He says:

My belief is that our bodies are designed to eat meat and that meat is an integral part of our diet. We evolved essentially as hunters, which means we need high nutrient food for energy and stamina.

We have a short digestive through-put – we don't need to keep food in our bodies for a long time because we can extract a high proportion of nutrients from what we eat. Animals designed to be vegetarians have a different system: think of the cow with all its stomachs geared to deal with cellulose. The cow may thrive on grass but it spends all its time eating and regurgitating. We don't.

Meat is an important source of protein, iron, minerals and other trace elements. Red meat is not only one of the best ways of getting easily absorbed iron, it also increases the absorption of iron from vegetables and cereals when eaten at the same time.

A lot of animal fat is bad for us, but it's perfectly possible to separate meat eating from fat eating

---

Lack of iron causes anaemia, which means a patient is pale, tired, lacks stamina and finds it hard to concentrate or think clearly. It can cause growth retardation and problems in pregnancy.

Vitamin B12 deficiency can be another problem if you don't have meat in your diet and can lead to neuropathy, or disease of the nerves, with weakness, loss of sensation, pins and needles and the inability to perform fine movements. In the worst cases the effects can be permanent.

There can also be a lack of other things like zinc, which promotes wound healing and fights infection. You can get zinc from vegetables but the best source is still meat.

There has been a disturbing rise in the incidence of certain diet-related conditions, especially among pregnant women, adolescents and young children. Babies' iron stores begin to run out at four to six months, and young children undergo rapid growth and development so they need extra nutrients, as do boys and girls at puberty. Teenagers should be particularly wary of going vegetarian in order to be slim.

About 15 per cent of my patients are of Asian origin and a high proportion of them are vegetarians and vegans who follow these diets for cultural and religious reasons. I see a substantial amount of iron and vitamin deficiency among them, and I have to prescribe vitamin supplements.

Of course it's possible to survive without animal products but meat has an important part to play in a balanced diet. The recent attitude that red meat especially is inherently bad for you, and that you'll get cancer and heart disease and high cholesterol, worries me because it's just not true.

The studies which have suggested it are not terribly scientific in that it's very difficult in whole population studies to assess what's going on. Certain lifestyles may include other factors as well. People who do not eat meat may not smoke, may drink less and exercise more.

As a doctor I have to assess an individual's risks of heart disease from a number of factors, including smoking, weight and family history. Diet is one factor and only increases in importance if all the others begin to stack up.

A lot of animal fat is bad for us, but it's perfectly possible to separate meat eating from fat eating – and meat is much leaner nowadays.

Over the past 20 years, we've seen the growth of the concept that we all ought to be concerned about staying well and looking after our health. This is all very desirable, but it does need a terrific amount of knowledge and even professionals have difficulty in managing it. Things aren't always clear-cut.

I've had patients say: 'I've given up meat, doctor' as if that's it, the answer to everything. Linda McCartney was obviously an intelligent woman but I think she was as concerned about farming practices as she was about health.

As a family we still eat and enjoy meat. I don't want half a cow on my plate, but a piece of sirloin or lamb is superb in every way. © *Daily Mail April, 1998*

Meat in the diet

Essential or optional?

BRITISH Nutrition FOUNDATION

At a recent British Nutritional Foundation seminar, Professor Tom Sanders (King's College, London) discussed whether meat was essential to the diet. In his opening comments he suggested that when considering this issue both political (health, welfare, environmental and economic) and personal (ethical, and freedom of choice) aspects were important. A decrease in red meat intake may lead to an increase in poultry consumption which could result in food poisoning from Salmonella. From a welfare point of view it could also be argued that lamb and beef are reared under better conditions than pork and poultry. Also parts of the UK are unsuitable for arable production. If the land was not used for grazing animals there would be no alternative use for it, and this could lead to a negative economic impact on communities in these areas.

Vegetarians are often shown to be healthier than meat eaters, however this may be due to confounding factors such as lower BMI, lower plasma cholesterol levels, lower factor VII coagulant activity and lower blood pressure. Vegetarians are also more health conscious with higher fibre and starch intakes and higher plasma ß-carotene and vitamin E levels. Activities such as smoking and drinking alcohol tend to be less common. Avoidance of meat certainly reduces the risk of CHD4, although consumption of lean fully trimmed meat has been shown to have no cholesterol raising effect.

Meat makes a useful nutritional contribution to intakes of retinol, vitamin B12, long chain PUFA, protein, iron and zinc. More recently meat has also been found to be a good source of vitamin D. A reduction in meat intake could lead to a reduction in intakes of long chain fatty acids and vitamins B12 and D. However a modest increase in consumption of oily fish such as mackerel or sardines, a rich source of these nutrients, would easily compensate.

A diet devoid of meat can be nutritionally adequate. However it is easier to obtain all the nutrients needed for health if the diet contains meat

---

Meat is a very good source of readily absorbed iron and vegetarian toddlers and women of reproductive age have been shown to have low iron stores (ferritin) despite having adequate iron intakes. This may develop into a problem if additional stresses such as pregnancy or heavy menstrual losses occur. A low ferritin level during pregnancy is associated with a low birth weight and lower iron stores in the infant. An iron supplement may be desirable for vegetarian women during pregnancy. Within the population, if meat intakes were reduced this would be likely to lead to an increased prevalence of iron deficiency anaemia.

In conclusion, a diet devoid of meat can be nutritionally adequate. However it is easier to obtain all the nutrients needed for health if the diet contains meat. If a policy were to be implemented to reduce red meat consumption, this would need to be accompanied by sound education to ensure avoidance of nutritional deficiencies. A food fortification strategy may also become necessary.

• The above is an extract from the *BNF Nutrition Bulletin* Vol. 22, Winter 1997. See page 41 for address details.

© *The British Nutritional Foundation January, 1998*

Big meat eaters cancer warning

By Jenny Hope, Medical Correspondent

An unprecedented official warning to eat less red meat to avoid cancer is to be issued by the Government.

It is the first time any country has attempted to tell its population how to make informed choices about food in order to cut the risk of developing the disease.

The alert, which will also include advice to eat more fruit, vegetables, and starchy fibre-rich foods, follows a report on the link between diet and cancer from Government-appointed health experts due to be published within the next few weeks.

The food industry and the meat producers in particular – already suffering the effects of the BSE crisis – are now bracing themselves for another wave of public concern.

Evidence of a link between diet and cancer has been growing in recent years although there is still disagreement among experts about the healthiest foods and also conflicting evidence about the contribution red meat actually makes to the disease.

But, controversially, the report from the Committee on Medical Aspects of Food Policy (COMA) targets heavy meat eaters – defined as those who rarely eat meals without any form of meat, particularly red meat.

Publication of the COMA report coincides with another, from the World Cancer Research Fund, which gives a similar message. Its 'global report', to be launched first in Britain and then in the US and India, is based on 4,000 pieces of existing research. It is understood the two reports are being released in Britain at the same time because their messages complement each other.

COMA was appointed to advise the Government on different aspects of the nation's eating habits. It has produced a series of authoritative reports ranging from fat in the diet to breastfeeding.

The Meat and Livestock Commission has not yet seen the latest report. But a spokesman said: 'We would point out that earlier COMA reports have highlighted that meat plays an important part of a balanced diet.'

About 273,000 Britons are diagnosed each year with cancer which kills one in four victims.

One distinguished scientist, Professor Sir Richard Doll, who first linked smoking and cancer, estimates that at least one-third of fatal cancers are linked to diet. He said last night: 'It is a significant cause of cancer, although the causes and effects are not as clear as one would like.'

Several studies had shown a link between bowel cancer and eating large amounts of meat. But he admitted the picture was confused because other studies showed no reduced incidence of the disease among vegetarians. 'The evidence is inconclusive,' he said.

There are around 30,000 cases of bowel cancer a year and half the victims die. It is the second biggest killer behind lung cancer.

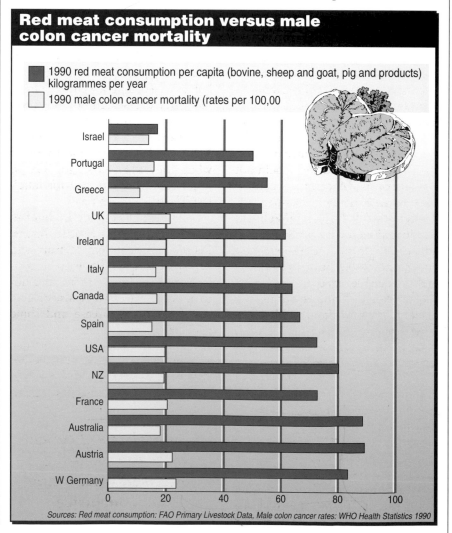

Red meat consumption versus male colon cancer mortality

■ 1990 red meat consumption per capita (bovine, sheep and goat, pig and products) kilogrammes per year

□ 1990 male colon cancer mortality (rates per 100,00

Israel, Portugal, Greece, UK, Ireland, Italy, Canada, Spain, USA, NZ, France, Australia, Austria, W Germany

0   20   40   60   80   100

Sources: Red meat consumption: FAO Primary Livestock Data, Male colon cancer rates: WHO Health Statistics 1990

Bowel and stomach cancer have the worst rate of survival of any cancers. About 11,000 people develop stomach cancer each year and two out of three die.

But a picture of the typical stomach cancer victim shows that keen carnivores may be at risk not so much because of the meat they eat but for what they miss out. Stomach cancer is linked to a poor diet with too much salt and fat and not enough fresh fruit and vegetables, which have an antioxidant effect.

The typical victim is an older man, of a generation who believed red meat was essential for health. He may eat plenty of meat and potatoes but skimp on greens and be suspicious of lower-fat alternatives such as chicken and fish. The salt in smoked and cured meats such as bacon and

> *The Japanese have among the highest rates of stomach cancer in the world despite eating very little meat, preferring fish*

sausages may also cause problems.

Women, who generally eat more white meats and vegetables, are less likely to suffer.

Experts point out however that the Japanese have among the highest rates of stomach cancer in the world despite eating very little meat, preferring fish.

Doctors now suspect the disease is closely linked to an ulcer bug which up to a third of the population carries, but may be triggered by poor diet, heavy smoking and drinking.

- Additional reporting: James Clark.

© *The Daily Mail*
September, 1997

Fruit and two veg, anyone?

Doctor at large. By Luisa Dillner

We are about to be told by the Government to eat less red meat to avoid cancer, if the *DailyMail*'s front page story (see opposite page) is to be believed. The *Mail*'s revelation that red meat is bad comes from two leaked reports, one from the Government's Committee on Medical Aspects of Food Policy (COMA), the other from the World Cancer Research Fund.

Most days there is media advice on what you should and should not eat and drink. Much of it is contradictory and therefore exasperating (only last week the private Wellman clinic said men who ate little or no meat were prone to fatigue and looked pale). On the other hand the public can be exasperating in its expectations. While resenting the nannying messages from health ministers to eat precise quantities of certain foods they still want definitive answers on what is and isn't good for them.

The *New England Journal of Medicine* was recently driven to write an editorial on the problems of what the public should believe about clinical research. 'No sooner do they hear the results of one research study then they hear of one with the opposite message. They substitute margarine for butter only to learn that margarine may be worse for their arteries.' An editorial on the margarine debate in the *New York Times* essentially asked, why can't researchers get it right the first time?

Researchers and medical journals often point out plaintively that what they publish is not the truth but a piece of a jigsaw puzzle. This is more true of research into nutrition than some other scientific areas because bias is so hard to eliminate. Many studies ask people to recall what they ate years ago. Try to remember what you had for lunch last Thursday. It isn't easy.

The effects of diet are hard to tease out from other healthy habits. People who eat lots of fruit and vegetables are also likely to be non-smokers, to exercise more, and not to be obese. All of which also protect you from heart disease and some cancers.

Even so the existing evidence suggests diet is heavily implicated in the development of some cancers. Sir Richard Doll, who first teased

> *Comparisons of cancer rates in vegetarians and meat-eaters are not conclusive*

out the deadly relationship between cigarettes and lung cancer, estimates it is the largest single risk factor – up to 35 per cent, compared to cigarettes at 30 per cent. The problem being that cause and effect are not so readily established in diet and cancer.

Apart from asking people with cancers to remember what they ate (typically they prejudice the results by recalling what they suspect was bad for them) and comparing their diet to people who haven't got the disease, researchers have looked at the effects of diet on animals and compared cancer rates in different countries.

In Japan, for example, stomach cancer rates are high, which is partly attributed to their penchant for smoked, processed food. Yet prostate cancer rates are low, perhaps due to their diet of rice and tofu (a soya bean product), which contain phyto-oestrogens – substances that may inhibit the growth of cancers. Soya has been shown to inhibit the growth of prostate cancer cells in mice.

Comparisons of cancer rates in vegetarians and meat-eaters are not conclusive. A study of more than 120,000 people in the Netherlands found a slightly increased risk of bowel cancer with processed meats (more than 15g a day) – blamed mainly on sausages. A Japanese study showed an increased risk of bowel cancer in people who frequently ate meat and rarely ate vegetables. The relationship between meat and cancer growth was explored in a paper published in the *Lancet* last year from Australia. Its findings suggested that some people were genetically more at risk of bowel cancer from eating meat than others – depending on whether or not they had an enzyme that rapidly inactivated cancer-promoting by-products.

However suggestive the evidence that meat may not be terribly good for you is, it is nothing like as strong as that for the protective effects of eating fruit and vegetables (as long as they're nor macerated by traditional British cooking). Fruit and vegetables protect against digestive and respiratory cancers.

Other, more conclusive advice may be available in a few years time from a Europe-wide study of diet and cancer – the biggest ever undertaken.

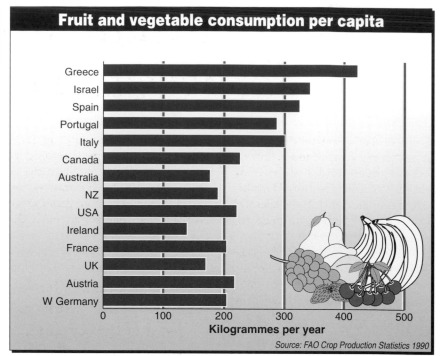

Fruit and vegetable consumption per capita

Kilogrammes per year

Source: FAO Crop Production Statistics 1990

Meanwhile, whatever the Government advises on meat, we are slowly shunning it anyway. According to the Vegetarian Society around 5,000 people a week are becoming vegetarians. But basic market research shows the ambiguity of self-definition. One survey yesterday said that nearly half of the people who call themselves vegetarians occasionally eat meat.

© *The Guardian*
September, 1997

50 per cent are eating less meat

Reports by Roger Highfield, Robert Uhlig and Aisling Irwin

More than 50 per cent of Britons are cutting meat consumption, prompting scientists to convert plant proteins into new foods with textures and tastes unlike anything known today.

Concern about animal welfare, and the health effects and fat content of meat, have led record numbers to cut the amount of meat they eat, Dr David Baines, an independent food scientist, told the British Association for the Advancement of Science, meeting in Leeds.

Although only four per cent of Britons are vegetarian, seven per cent have cut out red meat and 40 per cent often eat vegetarian meals. Even more Britons may have adopted a partially or wholly vegetarian diet than figures suggest because research was conducted before the BSE crisis.

The market for vegetarian foods is one of the fastest growing in the food industry, worth £400 million a year. 'The fastest growth has been seen in vegetarian burgers and grills, which have increased by 139 per cent in five years,' said Dr Baines.

'Twenty years ago you had to be a dedicated vegetarian to eat a veggie-burger – they were like packaged cardboard. Now it's a pleasant eat because of improvements in food technology.'

Before the BSE crisis, several manufacturers refused to make vegetarian products. Now those makers have several vegetarian products on supermarket shelves.

Arrum, a new artificial meat-like foodstuff made from wheat gluten and pea protein, with the bite characteristics, texture, flavour and look of animal flesh, is about to go on sale.

It blends amino acids from pulse and cereal proteins to ensure an adequate supply of all the proteins the body needs for growth.

Scientists at the Institute of Food Research in Reading developed Arrum by connecting electrodes to people's jaws to compare eating patterns from meat.

'Texturally and nutritionally, it is the equivalent to meat but only a tenth of its calories come from fat, whereas in beef it is around half.

'However, the nearer you get to meat, the more a certain part of the population reject it. For these people, the industry is developing totally new and unique foods.'

© *Telegraph Group Limited,*
London 1997

The Christian argument for vegetarianism

It is well known that during the last thirty years or more, farmers have been under increasing pressure to tailor traditional farming methods to the needs of cost-effective production. Farming animals intensively has become the norm.

It seems to me the only satisfactory basis on which we can oppose systems of close confinement is by recourse to the argument drawn from theos-rights. To put it at its most basic: animals have the right to be animals. The natural life of a Spirit-filled creature is a gift from God. When we take over the life of an animal to the extent of distorting its natural life for no other purpose than our own gain, we fall into sin. There is no clearer blasphemy before God than the perversion of his creatures.

To the question: 'Why is it wrong to deny chickens the rudimentary requirements of their natural life, such as freedom of movement or association?' there is, therefore, only one satisfactory answer: since an animal's natural life is a gift from God, it follows that God's right is violated when the natural life of his creatures is perverted. Those who, in contrast, opt for the welfarist approach to intensive farming are inevitably involved in speculating how far such and such may or may not suffer in what are plainly unnatural conditions. But unless animals are judged to have some right to their natural life, from what standpoint can we judge abnormalities, mutilations or adjustments? Confining a de-beaked hen in a battery cage is more than a moral crime; it is a living sign of our failure to recognise the blessing of God in creation.

What makes this situation all the more lamentable is the realisation that the use to which animals are put in intensive farming goes far beyond even the most generous interpretation of need. It will be obvious that humans can live healthy, stimulating and rewarding lives without white veal, pâté' de foie gras, or the ever-increasing quantities of cheap eggs. The truth is that we can afford to be much more generous to farm animals than is frequently the case today.

> **Since animals belong to God, have value to God and live for God, then their needless destruction is sinful**

Churches need to reflect in their own collective actions the sensitivity they frequently hope for in others. [In England], under present legislation, animals can be subject to intensive farming and are so on Church land. It is anomalous that the Church of England should allow on its land farming practices which many senior ecclesiastics oppose and which one bishop recently likened to an Auschwitz for animals.

The Christian argument for vegetarianism then is simple: since animals belong to God, have value to God and live for God, then their needless destruction is sinful. In short: animals have some right to their life, all circumstances being equal. That it has taken Christians so long to grasp this need not worry us. There were doubtless good reasons, partly theological, partly cultural and partly economic, why Christians in the past have found vegetarianism unfeasible. We do well not to judge too hastily, if at all. We cannot relive others' lives, or think their thoughts, or enter their consciences. But what we can be sure about is that living without what Clark calls 'avoidable ill' has a strong moral claim upon us now.

Some will surely question the limits of the vegetarian world here envisaged. Will large-scale vegetarianism work in practice? I confess I am agnostic, surely legitimately, about the possibility of a world-transforming vegetarianism. But clairvoyance is not an essential prerequisite of the vegetarian option, and what the future may hold, and its consequences, cannot easily be determined from any perspective. What I think is important to hold on to is the notion that the God who provides moral opportunities is the same God who enables the world, slowly but surely, to respond to them. From a theological perspective, no moral endeavour is wasted so long as it coheres with God's purpose for his cosmos.

• Excerpted from the book: *Christianity and the Rights of Animals*, (Crossroad Publ. Co., NY)

© Rev. Dr. Andrew Linzey
Director of Studies, Centre for the Study
of Theology, University of Essex

Wear the shoes, eat the bacon sandwich

Vegetarianism is becoming an increasingly popular option in the Anglo-Saxon world. Simon Titley questions the assumptions behind the rejection of meat and asks whether vegetarians are entitled to the moral high ground.

Close your eyes and imagine a bacon sandwich. Imagine the smell of the bacon as it cooks in the pan. Imagine the bread (white sliced, of course), moist with bacon fat. Imagine the unmistakable salty, meaty taste as you take your first bite. Salivating? Don't worry, you're in good company.

Roughly 90% of us enjoy eating dead animals. And why not? We are naturally carnivorous creatures and meat has formed part of the human diet ever since Homo Sapiens climbed down from the trees.

Yet attitudes to the consumption of animal flesh are being challenged.

Symbolic of the zeitgeist was the news that pork consumption in the USA fell by 20% following the screening of the new movie *Babe* (which features a talking piglet).

Animal welfare is perhaps the most persuasive argument deployed by vegetarians against the consumption of animals. When I drafted the Liberal Democrat green paper on animal welfare in 1992, however, it struck me that the crucial issue was not whether we kill animals for food but how we treat them while they are still alive.

The greatest scandal in terms of British animal welfare occurs in the poultry industry, where millions of chickens and turkeys are kept in appalling conditions to supply a demand for cheap meat and eggs. But are the protesters out picketing turkey factories? Are they highlighting the issue of battery-produced eggs? No, they're more concerned about the morality of eating veal or the fate of seal cubs.

Veal calves and seal cubs, with their pathetic doe eyes, appeal more easily to public sympathy, and are thus more effective as fund-raising and publicity-generating devices. I hate to say this, but the number of veal calves packed in crates is a tiny fraction of the number of chickens suffering in factory farms. But then chickens aren't very cuddly, are they? Apparently few people care about miserable, diseased chickens, no matter how great the industrial scale of the suffering.

Animals can feel pain, but they have no capacity for abstract thought

---

And this reveals the main weakness in the central plank of vegetarianism. By emphasising the morality of whether or not we should kill animals, rather than how we treat animals while they are alive, vegetarians serve an anthropomorphic agenda, a Walt Disney view which grades the worth of animals according to how cuddly they are.

I happen to care about how we husband our livestock. Quite apart from welfare considerations, when animals have been properly cared for, their meat tastes better. I refuse to buy cheap frozen chicken or turkey because I am aware of the cruelty that goes into the production of this food. But I also refuse to buy it because it tastes inferior. When I want to roast a chicken, I buy a free-range, corn-fed bird, partly for moral reasons, but also because I want quality food with real flavour, not bland pap from scraggy, diseased animals.

We do animals no favours by projecting our own values onto them. Animals can feel pain, but they have no capacity for abstract thought. Unlike humans, they do not take an existential view. The lamb you ate last Sunday, whatever else it went through, did not have its life chances dashed when it was slaughtered. A promising future career as a computer programmer was not brought to a premature end. Indeed, were it not

for the market for meat, that lamb would never have existed in the first place.

Vegetarianism fails adequately to address the issue of animal welfare, because it focuses on death, not on life. By choosing to buy humanely-reared chickens and refusing to buy factory-farmed ones, I am doing more to advance the cause of animal welfare than someone who eats no meat.

Vegetarians also argue that rearing animals for meat is an inefficient use of arable land, which raises world grain prices and leads to third world starvation. So far as large-scale beef production is concerned, this may be a valid argument. But it is an argument for eating less meat, not for eating no meat.

The production of pork or chicken, for example, even under humane conditions, requires relatively little land. Pigs, reared free range, can forage for food in woodland, and provide an economic justification for replanting trees on farmland. More importantly, sheep and goats provide a means of farming marginal land, which would be no use for growing arable crops.

A complete abstinence from meat, far from resolving the problem of third world starvation, would instead reduce the amount of land on the planet available for the production of food. A far more effective solution would be for people in developed nations to scale down their beef consumption and instead consider beef as an occasional treat.

Vegetarians believe that eating meat is unhealthy, and the high incidence of heart disease and cancer in northern European nations is cited as evidence for this. But consider the French paradox. The French eat a diet which is as high in meat as ours, yet suffer a much lower rate of heart disease, even in Normandy with a cuisine rich in butter and cream.

The answer is probably that the French diet is leavened with red wine (a known antidote to high cholesterol) plus a healthy dose of fish, vegetables and fruit. In Scotland, where there is the highest incidence of heart disease in the world, the most notable thing about the diet is not how much meat is eaten but how little fresh fruit and vegetables.

It is widely recognised that the healthiest diet is a Mediterranean one, with red wine, olive oil, pasta, fruit, vegetables, and (whether you like it or not) fish and meat. Less red meat than we in Britain tend to eat, admittedly, but meat nonetheless. It is not meat *per se* that is unhealthy, but an unbalanced diet.

And what have vegetarians to say about the positive contribution of fish to a healthy diet? Oily fish (such as mackerel), in particular, play an important part in combating heart disease. And if self-styled 'health food' is so healthy, why are half the shelves in the average health food shop stocked, not with real food, but vitamin supplements and quack remedies?

By all means avoid beef if you want to. Boycott haddock. Abstain from celery. But don't assume the moral high ground

---

Vegetarians tend to assume the moral high ground but most of them lack a morally consistent position. We've all met them. The 'vegetarian' who won't eat meat but will eat fish. The 'vegetarian' who eats neither meat nor fish, but will happily eat battery-farmed eggs or cheese containing animal rennet. The 'vegetarian' who won't touch meat, fish or eggs, but drinks milk without a thought for what might be going on in the dairy industry. The 'vegetarian' who will eat no animal products but walks around in leather shoes.

Since most vegetarians consume dairy produce, I'd like to know what alternative use they propose for surplus male calves. Have they ever tried milking a bull? That's why I admire vegans. They're loonies, but at least they're morally consistent loonies.

The popularity of vegetarianism in Britain today tells us far more about the confused state of Anglo-Saxon morality than it does about concern for animal welfare. The growing popularity of vegetarianism is a product not just of anthropomorphism but also of our squeamishness and puritanism.

Squeamishness is a product of urbanisation. We British were industrialised nearly 200 years ago, long before most of our European neighbours. Most of us have lost touch with how meat and fish are produced. A reluctance to handle raw meat and raw fish helps make highly-processed animal flesh more popular. Many British people kid themselves that they are eating less meat, when in fact they're eating just as much, but in the form of microwavable cheeseburgers, a frozen 'Hawaiian-style Pizza', or perhaps a 'Chicken Korma For One'.

This squeamishness, paradoxically, makes the animal welfare situation worse, not better. The meat that goes into such processed, 'value-added' foods is much more likely to come from dubious sources. By avoiding buying meat and fish in its raw state, consumers are thinking only of themselves.

Our puritanism is deeply ingrained and part of our Protestant heritage. It lends respectability to any form of self-denial. Why else would most vegetarian restaurants be such joyless places, with hard seats and harsh lighting, in which food seems to be eaten as a penance? The contrast with Catholic southern Europe, where food is a source of daily communal celebration, is marked. No wonder vegetarianism has never really caught on there.

If you want to be a 'vegetarian', that's fine by me. I'm a Liberal, and I respect individual choice. Individuals should be free to choose whether or not to eat meat, or fish, or Brussels sprouts for that matter. But there is a difference between your personal lifestyle preferences and any practical political option.

So by all means avoid beef if you want to. Boycott haddock. Abstain from celery. But don't assume the moral high ground. And have the honesty to distinguish between your subjective feelings, and practical actions likely to improve the lot of farm animals or fellow human beings.

© *Liberator Publications*

Meat cheats fry in the face of being veggie

By Sean Poulter, Consumer Affairs Correspondent

Half of Britain's vegetarians are secret meat-eaters, according to a survey.

Fifty-eight per cent admit they eat chicken fairly regularly, 52 per cent say they have fish, while bacon is enjoyed by 42 per cent – usually as breakfast or in a sandwich.

The figures – hotly disputed by the Vegetarian Society – seem to contradict claims that vegetarianism is massively on the increase as people turn away from meat. A multi-million pound industry has built up on the back of the apparent swing, with food firms such as Linda McCartney's enjoying a boom.

But if the independent research is correct, some 1.75 million of the three million Britons who claim to be vegetarians are closet carnivores.

The findings will feature in a £2million advertising campaign by the Danish bacon company, poking fun at virtuous vegetarians.

In a television commercial, people are seen being lured off the street and out of a wholefood restaurant to a café where bacon is being cooked – unable to resist the aroma. Roadside posters will incorporate a moving counter – said to be registering the constantly falling numbers of those who say they do not eat meat.

> **If the independent research is correct, some 1.75 million of the three million Britons who claim to be vegetarians are closet carnivores**

The research was conducted by the Taylor Nelson AGB Family Food Panel – a twice-yearly survey of 4,000 households, including 11,000 individuals. It found 56.2 per cent of vegetarians aged 35 to 44 eat meat, compared to 35 per cent of 25 to 34-year-olds.

Vegetarianism has been particularly associated with young girls. However the research showed 43.9 per cent of females under 25 who claim to be vegetarians eat meat, compared to 37.2 per cent of males.

Some 38 per cent said they were most likely to have bacon to start the day, 15 per cent enjoyed a bacon sandwich, five per cent used it as an ingredient and 42 per cent ate it in some other way.

Yesterday, the Vegetarian Society said the research sounded flawed. 'Other very specific and detailed research has suggested there are more than 3.5million fully-committed vegetarians in this country,' said spokesman Chris Dessent.

'Five thousand people a week are becoming vegetarian. The fastest growth rate is among 16 to 35-year-olds. It seems companies are getting desperate when they have to target vegetarians and try and entice us back to eating meat. It shows what an impact we are having on the entire food industry.

'If anything, this is a recognition of the power of vegetarianism. We have them on the run.'

© *The Daily Mail*
March, 1998

Breaking it gently

It has taken you a long time to build up the courage to tell your parents that you have joined a rapidly expanding group of the population . . . you have decided to take the plunge and become a vegetarian.

So you think it's going to be easy? Rather than being overjoyed, to your dismay, your parents are over the top in hysteria and very dismissive. And the battle has only just begun . . .

It is Sunday afternoon, you and your family are sitting down to eat the traditional roast dinner, meat and two veg, that has taken all morning to prepare. As the others around the table start to eat, you, having spent a long time trying to work out the best way of telling your family, nervously and suddenly mutter the immortal words, almost hoping that no one will hear you. 'Mum, I can't eat this. I'm a vegetarian.' The room fills with silence. Everybody looks at you in horror and you sink further and further into your chair. As you begin to wish you had never spoken, Mum says 'jolly good, now carry on and eat your dinner before it gets cold and don't be so stupid – and I mean all of the dinner'.

It is something that all of us have probably been through at one time or another, and for any would-be veggies it is something that they have got to look forward to. Even those of us who have followed a vegetarian lifestyle for many years now, still face major battles with our parents and older friends and relations. All too often we hear about people who have tried to become veggies but have been stopped by their parents or have been scared by whimsical myths about vegetarian diets being nutritionally bankrupt and very bad for one's health.

Parents in particular were created to worry, and this is what they do best. Their first reaction to anything that they know little about or personally disagree with is that it must be something bad and unhealthy. Vegetarianism is a concept increasing in popularity at a remarkable rate but think about when your parents were young; there were considerably fewer veggies about, and facts about vegetarianism were even more scarce and corrupt than they are today. This said, try imagining how your grandparents must feel about the whole idea!

> *How many other vegetarians, like myself, find the smell of meat, and the taste of meat substitutes, quite repulsive?*

For Mum or Dad, who probably only want what is best for you, the thought of having to cook meat-free culinary delights that are both tasty and nutritious is an absolute nightmare. So, you can help them along a bit: instead of announcing your news after a meaty meal has been made, try talking to your parents beforehand. I told my Mum going round the local supermarket as we passed the vegetarian section: that way Mum was able to see what sort of veggie food was on offer, and the prospect was not quite as daunting. Suggest that you help to cook your meals – there is nothing that goes down better than the offer of an extra pair of hands in the kitchen!

You need to make sure that you know yourself why you are becoming a vegetarian and you need to know enough about vegetarianism to prove that you are responsible enough to take control of your own diet. Try to show your family some books and leaflets, but ensure that you are subtle and gently introduce them to the idea.

Believe it or not, it is quite common to find that after the teenage son or daughter in a family becomes a vegetarian, most, if not all of the family (even those who at the outset appeared to be adamantly anti veggie) are soon converted. In my case, some six or seven years on, I remain the only convert, with the hamster as my only soul-mate although the rest of my family do eat veggie food quite often. (Usually the stuff that I buy and then find that I absolutely hate!)

Just suppose that your parents eventually accept the idea – I am still sceptical about their motives. Often their next tactic is to cook what they claim are completely meat-free meals but what the unaware new veggie does not realise is that the

'minced tvp' that. Mum claims to have bought, and which you have to admit tastes very realistic, is in fact real mince. And this is where all veggies come up against huge problems. I am very divided over the whole issue of meat-substitutes. I gave up meat and fish to follow a vegetarian diet and while these fake meats are useful for many meals, I do not particularly enjoy eating what could be, for all I know, real meat.

How many other vegetarians, like myself, find the smell of meat, and the taste of meat substitutes, quite repulsive? Surely I am not the only person who has to resort to getting packets out of the bin before I am one hundred per cent certain that I am not actually eating meat? I sincerely hope that somewhere, somebody recognises the need for a range of vegetarian foods that are vegetarian, not a range that is pretending that it is made from meat when it is not!

The issue over fish – to carry on eating it or not – is difficult and tricky. The alleged brain-food of the last generation, many people are divided over its benefits. Be aware of the propaganda that 'if you don't eat fish you will never be clever' because there is no real evidence to support it. Many parents like to try and compromise with their children. 'I've let you stop eating meat, but you are not going to give up fish as well.' Strictly the definition of a vegetarian states, according to the Vegetarian Society, that 'a true vegetarian is someone who eats no meat or meat-products, poultry, fish or slaughter-house by-products and who also eats free-range eggs . . .' Try to get round your parents by humouring them – agree to eat fish but when it actually comes to meals containing fish, discreetly push it to the side of the plate. Eventually parents get the message and gradually they will stop trying.

As for free-range eggs, the arguments for and against are endless but this is an issue where, unless Mum and Dad are veggie too, you could have a lot of problems. Ideally you should only eat free-range eggs, but they are more expensive and so Mum and Dad may only buy them if you agree to pay the difference. Then you need to try and find out whether ready-made foods are made with or without free-range eggs – believe me when I say it is a minefield, it is, and an absolute nightmare, but if you have ever seen pictures of battery farming and the appalling squalor that the hens are kept in, you will know that it is worth the effort.

As I said at the start, when you finally decide to tell your family, you are entering into a battle which will often go on for a very long time.

I have only considered problems inside the home – what about at school and when you eat out and when you go on holiday? While it can seem very lonely, remember that the Vegetarian Society is always ready to give support and advice. Keep on fighting for what you believe in and remember that even if there is nobody else who agrees with you, at least you know that what you are doing is right. And when you start to win through, the feeling of success and achievement outstrips everything that has gone before.

• Jamie Anderson is the Society's Youth Contact in the Wirral

© The Vegetarian Society

Wot no beef?

Nicole McSweeney reports on who's doing what for vegetarians in fast-food market.

There was a time when, if you walked into a fast-food chain like McDonalds and asked what was suitable for vegetarians, the assistant behind the counter would have said something along the lines of: 'Che? What did you say?' and then offered you a dried bun with a bit of lettuce and a slice of tomato. Slowly multi-national chains are coming round to the idea that the growing number of vegetarians provides a valuable market to tap into.

McDonald's
Staff at St Mary's Gate, Manchester, Customer Services, Head Office
Head Office Customer Services was able to confirm that everything is cooked in separate vats. The fries are cooked in rapeseed oil. The scrambled eggs on the breakfast menu are said to be free-range.

However it would be wise to assume that any egg ingredients in products which are bought pre-packed from suppliers are unlikely to be free-range because they are said to be too expensive for bulk manufacture.

There is not much available for vegetarian children yet. The Vegetarian Deluxe meal deal is only available in adult size at present, because it's a new option on test. It is worth asking at your local restaurant to see if a smaller burger could be made specially for a child.

The Vegetarian Deluxe consists of vegetables in breadcrumbs served in a bun with the usual choice of dressings and salad. Vegetarian cheese is served with these burgers.

The sundaes are vegetarian. A small amount of fish oil is used in lubricating the machinery when making the apple pies. Nothing was mentioned about the use of animal fats in their manufacture.

At the Manchester restaurant a member of staff first suggested a fish product on the grounds that 'many vegetarians eat fish'. It was also suggested that the apple pies (head office didn't confirm this) are made with mixed animal and vegetable fats and the doughnuts are made with egg yolk powder which is unlikely to be free-range.

Kentucky Fried Chicken

Staff at Hyde Road, Manchester, Marketing Manager, Head Office

Even though Kentucky Fried Chicken specialises in chicken, there is a veggie burger in the pipeline to attract the growing vegetarian market.

At present only fries (which are cooked separately in vegetable oil), corn on the cob, beans and coleslaw (which has battery eggs in the mayonnaise) are available. Desserts consist of apple pies (which are cooked in vegetable oil) and Viennetta ice cream.

Burger King

Staff at Market Street, Manchester, Marketing Manager, Manchester, Head Office

The spicy bean burger is vegetarian and is cooked separately from other products. The fries are cooked in hydrogenated vegetable oil. They cannot be guaranteed free from cross contamination, i.e. bean burgers may be cooked in the same vat as meat products by accident or the same utensils may be used for different foods at busy times.

For desserts, the ice cream is vegetarian but the apple pies contain gelatin (which the Burger King staff failed to mention).

An Every Day Value Meal is available with bean burger, regular fries and regular drink, which is in a similar price range to the other burgers.

No meal deals are available for vegetarian children, although meat-eating children can choose from meat or chicken.

At the restaurant I was told that although the spicy bean burger is cooked separately from the other burgers, it is cooked in the same vat as the chicken in most restaurants. The assistant at the Manchester restaurant I spoke to had previously worked at Chester where he said separate vats were always used.

Wimpy

Staff at the Arndale Centre, Manchester, Marketing Manager, Head Office

Wimpy does not claim that any product is vegetarian because there are no separate fryers designated for the various products and cross contamination is possible. The aim is that products are cooked separately but this may not be possible all the time. Chicken slices could be cooked in the same fat as the bean burger and cod clippers cooked in the same fat as the chips. The Marketing Manager confirmed that the cheese in the Vegetable and Cheese Nuggets is suitable for vegetarians. Vegetable oil is used to cook everything. The ice cream is made with palm kernel oil and vegetarian emulsifiers, providing a suitable dessert. At the Manchester restaurant staff said separate vats are used for all the products. The chips and side salad were described by restaurant staff as suitable for vegetarians.

There is a meal deal with the spicy bean burger, chips, and a drink. This is more expensive than other meal deals because the cost of buying the product is greater.

Pizzaland

Staff at Piccadilly, Manchester, Marketing Services Manager, Head Office

None of the cheeses used on the vegetarian pizzas contain animal rennet.

Butter is used on the garlic bread. The ice creams contain milk and whey. The source of the whey is unknown so it may or may not be suitable for vegetarians. It is doubtful that the eggs used in the mayonnaise

and the tiramisu are free-range as these are bought in bulk from outside suppliers.

There is a policy to keep the vegetable and meat toppings on different sides of the work surface and separate pizza cutters are used.

There is quite a wide choice for vegetarians at Pizzaland. The menu consists of Margarita (basic cheese and tomato), Vegetarian (a mixture of vegetable toppings) and the Four cheeses which are all vegetarian.

Starters include various salads, garlic bread, nachos, potato, mushroom, and tomato soup.

Pizza Hut

Production Specialist

Suitable starters for vegetarians include the mushroom stroganoff, salads, and two vegetable pasta dishes. None of the cheeses used contain animal rennet. Microbial rennet is used instead as this is recognised as being an important consideration for vegetarians. All the oils used are vegetable. Free-range eggs are not used in bought-in products. Strict procedures exist to avoid cross contamination of different food types.

Toppings are kept on different tables, different cutters are used and the pizzas are cooked separately.

All vegetarian dishes have a Pizza Hut V next to them on the menu indicating that they are suitable for ovo-lacto vegetarians.

So, the best advice for eating in fast-food outlets is – be observant and ask lots of questions (even at the risk of appearing fastidious!).

• *The Vegetarian* is published by The Vegetarian Society and is sent free of charge to all members.

© The Vegetarian Society

Pure murder?

Many students do not mince words about meat – but others eat it happily. Tim Nash and Steve Young stage a debate between vegetarians and carnivores

Every day another person turns to vegetarianism and vegetarian foods are more and more widely available in supermarkets and restaurants. In a Gair Rhydd debate we pitted two die-hard meat-eaters against two full-on vegetarians to see if either could convince the others to change.

Chris Holden has been a vegetarian for the past five years and a vegan for the past two.

'I saw a documentary on the TV about animal cruelty,' he says, 'which was really grim and made me decide to become a vegetarian. I started to learn about things like the milk trade and how it is connected with the meat industry. If you're going to have milk you have to have pregnant cows but where do all the baby cows go?

'They go to the European veal crates. Fifty per cent of chickens are egg layers and 50 per cent are not, so what happens to the second 50 per cent? They are killed in cruel ways,'

The unfortunately named Pete Cow has been a vegetarian for about eight years.

'From the environmental point of view,' says Cow, 'the production of meat uses up far more water and produces far more pollution than the production of cereals and grains. You can feed 61 people on a soya diet on the same amount of land that will feed two people on a meat diet.'

> ## 'I saw a documentary on the TV about animal cruelty, which was really grim and made me decide to become a vegetarian'

Jamie Moran admits that while he does think about where meat comes from, it will never change his eating habits. 'I just couldn't do without meat. I have been brought up on it and I like it.'

The main argument put forward by meat-eaters is that we need meat to get the energy, vitamins, minerals and protein our bodies require. But the vegetarians claim they get everything they need without meat.

'Vegetarians live longer and have fewer illnesses, especially cancer of the bowel and high blood pressure,' explains Holden. 'If I am not getting a balanced diet then why am I likely to live longer?' he adds.

Worry about BSE does not seem to be a major problem for our meat-eaters, the general view being that after 20 years of eating beef, the chances are it may already be in your system. If not, the next burger you eat won't make a difference.

'I don't worry about BSE because I don't eat the spinal cord of cows,' says Moran. 'I don't eat dodgy mince or dodgy burgers. I think it's important to know where you get your meat from and to go to a reputable butcher.'

Few meat-eaters could deny that the smell of bacon sizzling first thing in the morning is guaranteed to set the taste buds to overdrive, but do vegetarians ever hanker for a quick bacon sandwich when no one is looking?

'I feel incredibly guilty walking past fast-food places because it makes me hungry,' confesses Holden.

'I am not immune to the bacon sandwich smell but am never tempted. I have no regrets about becoming a vegetarian. I feel more healthy than ever before and am more sorted with my spiritual welfare, not in a religious sense, but I feel I am living how I believe. I don't believe in needless cruelty or bullying, so I don't do it.'

But our meat-eaters are still not

'I just couldn't do without meat. I have been brought up on it and I like it'

---

convinced. 'I don't really have a problem with the animal rights issue,' says Janine McCaster. 'I walk through

the countryside and see cows, but the idea that they are going to be killed for us to eat is not a problem for me.'

Moran agrees: 'I have worked in a butcher's and it was fine. Even if I wanted to I don't think I'd be strong enough to be a vegetarian.'

• A longer version of this piece appeared in *Gair Rhydd*, the University of Wales, Cardiff.
© *The Guardian*
March, 1998

Research reveals school confusion over vegetarianism

Information from the Vegetarian Society

Research by the Vegetarian Society has revealed that many children in primary and secondary schools are not being provided with adequate vegetarian school meals, and that there is a high level of confusion over the definition of what constitutes a vegetarian option.

The research was carried out with monitoring officers for school caterers as part of the Vegetarian Society's ongoing educational initiative. Two-thirds of the UK's 184 school contract caterers, providing meals for thousands of the UK's schools, were involved in the research.

The research revealed that 61% of schools' caterers could not define what being vegetarian means.

- 53% of respondents mistakenly included fish as a product suitable for vegetarians and a small number of caterers believed chicken and other white meat would be suitable for vegetarians.
- 76% of local authorities offered what they considered to be a vegetarian option daily both in

primary and secondary schools. 84% of schools' caterers followed some form of healthy eating policy.

'The provision of vegetarian school meals differs greatly. Many caterers are providing an excellent service to vegetarians, but others desperately need more knowledge about vegetarianism and vegetarian food.

'It is worrying that over half of school caterers consider fish to be

suitable for vegetarians. This may well come as a big shock to parents who expect their children to be given the choice to eat a vegetarian meal at school. There is a real need for official guidelines to be issued that define what is acceptable for vegetarians. The Vegetarian Society is very keen to work alongside school caterers in the future to ensure that the best possible service can be achieved for vegetarian children across the UK,' said Sara Ayres, Youth Education Officer for the Vegetarian Society.

The research also found that vegetarian options had an overreliance on cheese as a protein source, rather than including alternatives such as beans, soya products and lentils.

It is estimated that 12% of secondary school children and 5% of primary school children are vegetarian.

The total number of vegetarians in the UK stands at approximately 4 million. According to a Gallup poll of May 1997, the numbers are currently increasing at a rate of 5,000 per week.
© *The Vegetarian Society*
February, 1998

I'm sick of vegetarian hypocrisy

You don't eat meat and scorn those who do? Campaigning journalist and broadcaster James Erlichman calls your bluff

My childhood chum, Glen, and I were walking in the Arizona desert. We were there to rediscover stuff. All kinds of stuff. Walk miles and conversation is your only distraction. We talked about the early years of his marriage when I visited him in upper New York State where he worked, and still does, as a probation officer, keeping a few animals on a small holding. I remembered how his station wagon would sit in the driveway while his garage was a home for Hamburger, a steer Glen had raised for slaughter.

In the desert, trudging on, I asked what had happened to Hamburger. 'Oh, we fattened him up and sent him off to the local slaughter house,' Glen said.

'Did you eat him, any of him?' I asked.

'No way, couldn't eat Hamburger,' he said. 'We just took the money.'

I was smug. 'So you couldn't dare eat anything you had raised?'

'Oh that's no real problem,' said Glen. 'We kept pigs and chickens, and we ate them.' He described the slaughter of the pigs. 'Didn't like that much,' he said. 'Nice creatures, pigs. But I grabbed a handful of food and walked towards them with a rifle. They came up to me, took a snout of food and I blew their brains out. Hated it, tricking them. Awful.'

The chickens were easier. 'We had a chicken coop and I would grab the easiest one to catch. Took it outside, wrung its neck, cut its head off and then slit its guts with the feathers still on. Heaved the guts back in the coop and walked toward the kitchen. Can you believe it, the other chickens set about fighting over the guts. What disgusting creatures they are.'

I tell you all this because, as much as I love my childhood chum, the story sums up for me our frequent hypocrisy toward food production. OK, organic vegans, your hands are clean. If you eat no meat or animal products and never buy vegetables whose yield or cosmetic appearance have been improved by fertilisers and pesticides, then you can be excused from this outburst of anger.

I watched protesters drinking milk and eating bacon sandwiches at Shoreham and Brightlingsea while they bemoaned the fate of calves and sheep being trucked across the channel

---

But the rest of us have a lot to answer for, and I speak, not as an organic vegan socialist, but as a reluctant and rather ashamed capitalist carnivore. And conventional vegetarians, it is you who most deeply annoy me in the hypocrisy stakes.

Could someone please tell me what vegetarian virtue there is in consuming the animal products – milk, cheese, cream, yoghurt and eggs – in large quantities, of creatures – dairy cows and laying hens – that are subject to the most intense and cruel forms of animal agriculture? Better surely to kill them quickly for meat than to torture them while you vegetarians help siphon the protein from them, slowly. You don't escape just because you don't eat the flesh, for heaven's sake. It is as if the bank robber said: 'I enjoyed the proceeds from the hold-up, but I'm innocent because I did not pull the trigger.'

OK, so I have had my rant. That is what this delightful column is for and I am honoured to be asked to write for it. But the fact is that all of us – except organic vegans – have a lot to answer for. The real trick is that we have been distanced from food production, and especially the death of animals. We slaughter some 800 million beasts and poultry every year in Britain alone.

The food industry has helped us with this self-deception. Few of us buy meat from the butcher anymore. Most of us will remember buying a slab of meat from the counter, and the name and function was clear: BUTCHER. That was the previous generation. Then came the supermarket and the meat is in plastic packets with a coating of shrink wrap.

And now we have the ubiquitous ready-made meal: lasagnes, shepherd's pies and Thai green curries, those frozen and cook-chilled meals which grace the shelves of our upmarket supermarkets. People think they are avoiding meat, but total consumption does not fall. We are part of a quiet revolution which exists only in our minds.

I watched protesters drinking milk and eating bacon sandwiches at Shoreham and Brightlingsea while they bemoaned the fate of calves and sheep being trucked across the channel. The principal cruelty is to breed, incarcerate, raise and slaughter animals in their millions in the first place. Where you take them, adding relatively minor transport pain to their short, nasty lives, is almost neither here nor there.

Or, put most starkly: how do we cuddle our pets and yet kill for a great British breakfast?

© The Food Magazine
October-December 1995

Tricky questions, expert answers

Over the years at the Vegetarian Society and Animal Aid we've probably been asked every question meat-eaters can come up with

What would happen to all the animals if everyone went vegetarian?

Think of all those animals denied the right to be born by all those vegetarians who refuse to kill and eat them! What a silly argument.

The fact is that most of today's farm animals are genetically manipulated to put on weight at an enormous rate and to be killed as quickly as possible. This puts great strain on their limbs and they often suffer from leg weaknesses or suffer from diseases. So while it is true that they wouldn't exist at all if they weren't bred for meat, all this means in most cases is that they are spared a life of misery followed by a brutal death.

Although there would be fewer farm animals in a vegetarian world, there would still be enough land available for small numbers to live out their lives peacefully on well-managed sanctuaries.

Can I be a vegetarian and still wear leather?

Being veggie is about what you eat but many vegetarians also choose not to wear leather because it comes from dead animals. Ten per cent of the value of the animal is its skin. Leather and fur are really very much the same. Alternatives to leather – which don't scare your friends away with cheesy feet – are available!

Aren't all vegetarians pale and unhealthy?

The oldest myths die hardest! Prove 'em wrong by being the least pale, most healthy vegetarian yet! You could try pointing out that medical studies are proving that vegetarians are less likely to suffer from heart disease, cancer, diet-related diabetes, obesity and high blood pressure.

What do you eat then? Just vegetables?

You'll be amazed how often people will ask you this. Some people have this idea that being vegetarian means eating tons of raw or boiled vegetables. They can't get to grips with the fact that 'ordinary' stuff like pizzas, burgers and pies can be meat-free and just as tasty. Ask them to name five exciting, interesting meat dishes they've had in the last week and they will get stuck in no time!

Animals eat each other so what is wrong with eating them?

Think about it – we claim we're better than animals, that's why we kill them, and then try to explain away our behaviour by comparing ourselves back to animals again – very silly.

Don't you miss meat?

Aaaaargh! No! Say it as loudly and clearly as you are sure to feel it. What's to miss, eh?

What about when all my friends go to a burger bar?

None of the food on sale at burger bars is particularly healthy or nutritious, but for those who like to visit them there is usually something available for vegetarians. Even McDonalds have started to sell veggie burgers in some areas (it is vegan if you ask for the mayonnaise to be left off) and their fries are cooked in vegetable oil. Other burger bars, for example Burger King, also have veggie burgers (which are usually made with TVP but may be vegetable based). Eating out is much easier nowadays as most fast-food chains have veggie options on their menus. Watch out for the hidden ingredients though, like battery eggs, animal fats and animal-rennet cheese. Some restaurants now actually tell you which dishes are suitable for vegetarians and will even tell you the source of the cheese! The times they are a-changin'.

Do I need to take vitamin supplements?

Vitamin supplements shouldn't be necessary as long as you have a well-balanced diet. If you feel in need of supplements there are a number available from health food shops which are suitable for vegetarians but do get some advice on your diet as well. The Vegetarian Society and Animal Aid can both provide advice on diet and nutrition. Vitamin supplements may be useful during a change in your diet, for example when first becoming a vegetarian or during periods of ill health or recovery from illness. Try not to rely on them though. A vitamin B12 supplement may be helpful to vegans who choose not to eat foods which are fortified with this essential vitamin.

I enjoy sports. How could I keep up my strength and energy if I didn't eat meat?

The idea that vegetarians aren't as fit or as strong as meat-eaters is a myth. Many champion athletes are vegetarian, such as the tennis star Martina Navratalova and Olympic champion sprinter Carl Lewis. Vegetable protein is in things like beans, rice, bread, pasta, soya and nuts and it is just as good as meat protein. Just think about it – elephants and gorillas are vegetarian and they're not weaklings!

• The above is an extract from the Vegetarian Society's Web site. See page 41 for details.

© The Vegetarian Society
June, 1998

Being a veggie was murder

As increasing numbers turn their backs on meat, former animal rights campaigner Tim Samuels will be tucking into turkey for the first Christmas in 10 years. He explains why he's decided to give up beanburgers and make the switch back to beef – after a decade of being vegetarian.

For the majority of the population, the act of buying a cheeseburger at McDonald's is a relatively mundane procedure. But after a decade of abstinence from meat, making the purchase became a near-pornographic experience.

Standing in the queue warily eyeing up the McDonald's menu board, I was struck by a sensation first experienced around the mid-1980s when stretching for the magazine top shelf in a Manchester corner shop – the rush of adrenaline that heralds the triumph of carnal urge over poxy principle. The simple cheeseburger had been transformed into a smutty mag – a metamorphosis abetted by its being served in a brown paper bag.

Buying the burger represented a volte-face in my teenage relationship with McDonald's – which largely consisted of standing outside its restaurants handing out leaflets graphically depicting a cow upturned in an abattoir, blood gushing from its head, under the slogan: 'Would you still eat meat if it looked like this?' Back then vegetarianism took something of a quasi-religious status. Facts about the meat industry, detailed in the glossy literature issued by animal rights groups, carried the reverence of absolute truths. My vegetarianism acquired an evangelical zeal after being adopted as a 'youth spokesperson' by the Vegetarian Society, precipitating a series of cringing television appearances; the most retrospectively traumatic involved cooking a broccoli dish alongside Cheryl Baker on her Saturday morning kids' show *Eggs 'n' Baker* (marginally more embarrassing than preparing a veggie burger, of all things, for an ungracious Terry Christian). Compensation did come, however, with the opportunity to interview the Lord High Priest of Vegetarianism, Morrissey (naturally, a 'Meat is Murder' T-shirt was donned for the occasion).

There was something deeply satisfying about sacrificing vegetarianism by dining with the devil of days gone-by, Ronald McDonald

---

Back to the queue in McDonald's. Edging closer to the front – still no sign of remorse to make a last-minute killjoy appearance. However, a show of remorse would only really be allowed on grounds of nostalgia for an adolescent era, when idealism was the main player. But major changes in principles have taken place since then: idealism has been substituted off, scepticism is the new star striker in town. It took scepticism a while to settle in, but once it found form it was only a matter of time before vegetarianism was hounded off the pitch.

'Can I take your order please?' Only one obstacle now stood between me and my McDonald's: the scare stories. According to such legends, a sudden return to meat-eating prompts a violent bodily reaction: instant vomiting, days of diarrhoea – tales luridly deployed as the final defence to keep the potential defector inside the camp. Those afflicted by such complaints should have possessed the foresight to renounce their vegetarianism at a McDonald's. Picking a lovingly prepared 7oz sirloin steak is just asking for trouble, when opting for a cheeseburger even keeps open the possibility that no meat is going to be ingested. The first bite did rekindle certain memories amongst the taste-buds: not from the distant days of carefree childhood carnivorism, but of a Veggie Whopper last month at a Burger King by King's Cross station. It was something of a disappointment just how close the imitation burger had come to emulating the genuine article. Maybe a tad saltier, a little rougher to chew, but no major reunion with long-lost taste sensations. And no vomiting or diarrhoea.

Considering the sacrifice involved in maintaining principles, they are enticingly cheap to dispose of – 69p in this case. Having decided to make diet and belief congruous once again, there was something deeply satisfying about sacrificing vegetarianism by dining with the devil of days gone-by, Ronald McDonald.

© *The Independent*
December, 1997

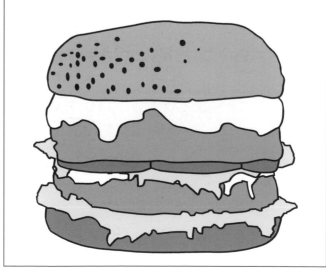

Meat the facts

We would like to ensure that you are not unnecessarily concerned through misinformation. By Tony Middlemiss

Red meat and health

Meat offers many nutritional benefits and thus a valuable role as part of a modern and balanced diet. Meat is rich in protein and provides us with essential minerals, particularly iron which is needed to make haemoglobin, the vital oxygen-carrying constituent of blood, as well as being one of our best sources of zinc, which is necessary for the immune system and healthy skin. Meat is also an important source of dietary B vitamins; it contains vitamin B12 which is not found in foods of vegetable origin, but is vital for healthy blood and nerves. One more significant fact – Britain has the highest rate of heart disease among EC countries, but the second lowest meat consumption per head. France has the highest meat consumption and the lowest heart disease rate!

Safety issues – legislation

The British meat industry is one of the most closely controlled and highly regulated industries in Europe. A total of over 50 pieces of European and UK legislation cover all aspects of meat safety from production through to retail sale.

The moral implications of eating meat

Eating meat is a way of life, and moral concerns are matters for individuals. We respect the right of individuals to choose not to eat meat but believe that the vast majority who choose to do so should not be made to feel guilty, for example, by 'special interest' pressure groups. Meat has always been part of our diet. The structure of our digestive system is evidence of this. Sir David Attenborough, the president of the British Association for the Advancement of Science, pointed out that humans have 'the teeth of an omnivore and the gut of certainly not a vegetarian'.

The number of vegetarians

Meat consumption is not declining, Government statistics show that meat consumption per head of the population has remained relatively static over the last 20 years. This can be seen in the consumption figures per head over the last two decades: 1970 – 62.2kg, 1980 – 63.4kg, 1990 – 65.4kg. But there are changes in the different meats and the balance between household and catering consumption. There is no evidence to suggest that the number of vegetarians is increasing. Independent research supports this statement.

Taylor Nelson:
- 99% of households consume meat in any two-weekly period. 93% of households consume meat at least twice a week.

National Health Survey:
- 3% of population in 1990 claimed to be vegetarians.
- 2% of population in 1991 claimed to be vegetarians.

Claims that young people are turning vegetarian are misleading. The growth of fast-food outlets such as McDonald's and Burger King, and their popularity among young people, suggest that the only difference between children and adults is how and when they eat meat. Surveys of eating habits of children consistently show burgers as the most popular choice.

Meat eating and the Third World issues

Eating less meat in the UK will not make more grain available for starvation relief overseas. Indeed, there is a surplus of grain in the world, so the problems are political rather than of supply. None of the ecological dangers facing the world has a direct relationship with meat eating. There is a world surplus of beef so there is no truth in the statement that rainforests are destroyed simply to provide grazing land to produce more beef.

© Tony Middlemiss

Vegetarians are less likely to die of heart disease

But not bowel cancer

Vegetarians are 24% less likely to die from ischemic heart disease than meat eaters, but do not have a decreased risk of dying from bowel cancer according to researchers from the Imperial Cancer Research Fund (ICRF). Their findings are published today (27 March) in *Public Health Nutrition*.*

The researchers pooled information from five existing studies which had recruited a large proportion of vegetarians: two studies in Britain, two in USA , and one in Germany. Altogether there were 76,000 men and women in the studies, of whom 28,000 were vegetarians.

The subjects were followed for an average of 11 years, after which there were 8,3000 deaths from all causes. The analyses compare the death rates in the vegetarians with those in the non-vegetarians in the same studies. This comprises essentially all the data available on deaths in Western-style vegetarians.

Said Dr Tim Key, research scientist with the ICRF Cancer Epidemiology Unit, Oxford: 'We found an even greater reduction in deaths from ischemic heart disease in younger vegetarians with 45% reduction below the age of 65. However, it only applied to vegetarians who had followed their diet for over five years.'

> *The study also found there wasn't any evidence that a vegetarian diet made any difference to the risk of dying from bowel cancer*

The team also divided the non-vegetarians into two groups – semi-vegetarians (those who only ate fish or ate meat less than once a week) and regular meat eaters (those who ate meat at least once a week) – and compared the regular meat eaters with vegetarians and semi-vegetarians. They found that, compared with regular meat eaters, there was a 22% decrease in deaths from ischemic heart disease in semi-vegetarians and a 34% decrease in the vegetarians.

The scientists believe that the most likely explanation for their findings is that vegetarians have lower levels of cholesterol in their blood.

The study also found there wasn't any evidence that a vegetarian diet made any difference to the risk of dying from bowel cancer.

'Some previous studies have suggested that high meat intakes might increase the risk of bowel cancer, but the evidence has been inconsistent. The absence of any difference between vegetarians and non-vegetarians in mortality from bowel cancer in our analysis suggests that meat itself may have little effect on the development of this disease. Other research has suggested that high intakes of vegetables, fruit and dietary fibre may reduce the risk of this cancer, but more research is needed,' explained Dr Key.

Deaths from breast, prostate, lung and stomach cancer were not significantly lower among vegetarians in this study either.

* 'Mortality in vegetarians: a collaborative analysis of 8,300 deaths among 76,000 men and women in five prospective studies.' *Public Health Nutrition*, 27 March 1998
© Imperial Cancer Research Fund (ICRF)

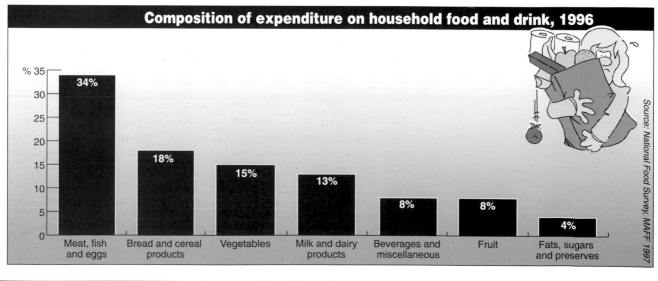

Composition of expenditure on household food and drink, 1996

- Meat, fish and eggs: 34%
- Bread and cereal products: 18%
- Vegetables: 15%
- Milk and dairy products: 13%
- Beverages and miscellaneous: 8%
- Fruit: 8%
- Fats, sugars and preserves: 4%

Source: National Food Survey, MAFF 1997

A record 3 million vegetarians in the UK

Information from Realeat

A record 5.4% of the population has now adopted a vegetarian diet, an increase of 20% over the figures in the 1995 Realeat Survey.

The means that there are now over 3 million vegetarians, and that the increase has been at a rate of 5,000 people every week for the last 2 years. Unlike previous surveys where women have led the way, there has been a 37% increase in vegetarian men since 1995!

Since 1984, when the Realeat Surveys began, 132,000 people every year have moved to a vegetarian lifestyle.

As might be expected, there has been a significant rise in the number of people who have removed red meat completely from their diet.

An all-time high of 14.3% of the population no longer eat red meat, over 8 million people, an increase of 1.4 million since 1995. This is an increase of 21% since 1995 and 258% since 1984.

13,000 people every week for the last 2 years have stopped eating red meat, and 18% of women are now non red meat-eaters.

Almost half the population (46%) are now actively eating less red meat. Along with the large rise in vegetarian men, over 51% of men are now actively eating less red meat, particularly in the age group 16-24, where this figure is over 74%!

As a motivation for eating less meat, BSE featured for the first time in the 1995 survey. At that time, 7% cited BSE as their primary health concern, and this has risen dramatically to nearly 22% in the 1997 survey.

Commenting on the results of the 1997 Realeat Survey, Graham Keen, Sales and Marketing Director of Realeat (part of the Haldane Foods Group), said:

One of the most interesting aspects of this survey is that it was conducted in March 1997, exactly one year after the outbreak of BSE in 1996. It has been argued by some that things were getting back to normal for the meat industry.

What these figures conclusively show is that this is not the case, and that record numbers of people are consciously making permanent changes to their lifestyle.

'13,000 people every week for the last 2 years have stopped eating red meat, but what is particularly striking is that 5,000 of these have moved all the way to a totally vegetarian diet.'

• The above is an extract from the press release of the Realeat Survey 1984 – 1997, *Changing Attitudes to Meat Consumption* conducted by the Gallup Organisation.

© *The Realeat Survey Office*

Myths about vegetarian food

'It takes a long time to cook'
Only if you want it to. There are lots of quick and easy meals you can prepare yourself: stir-fry vegetables with rice and tofu; all kinds of pasta dishes; dahl (spiced lentils) with chapatis; vegetarian burgers, chips and peas; even baked beans on toast.

'A vegetarian diet is boring'
It's not an act of self-sacrifice! A vegetarian diet can introduce a huge variety of healthy and interesting foods into your diet and whether you like Italian, Indian, Thai, Chinese, Mexican, Caribbean, Middle Eastern or Japanese food, there are loads of vegetarian dishes available in restaurants and as recipes in books and magazines. Many familiar meals (e.g. shepherd's pie, chilli con carne, casseroles, lasagnes and stews) can easily be adapted for vegetarians.

'It's natural for humans to eat meat'
It's natural for carnivorous animals like tigers to eat meat, but humans are not carnivores! We are omnivores, and can eat most foods. In other words we have a choice whether or not to kill for our food.

'We need meat to be strong and build muscle'
Stallions, gorillas and elephants don't do too badly on a vegetarian diet. Olympic champion runner Carl Lewis apparently achieved his success on a vegan diet and there are plenty of other vegetarian and vegan athletes proving that you don't need meat to build muscle, stamina or strength.

• The above is an extract from *Recipe for Life*, produced by Animal Aid. See page 41 for address details.

© *Animal Aid*

13,000 people per week give up red meat!

Information from Realeat

The 1995 Realeat Survey produced what was, at the time, a staggering statistic. 5,500 people per week, every week of the previous 2 years, had stopped eating red meat.

In this latest survey, which was conducted during March 1997, this figure has risen to an amazing 13,000 people every week giving up red meat.

There are now 8 million people, 14.3% of the population, who have removed red meat from their diet, compared with 6.6 million in 1995 and 2.2 million back in 1984, when the first survey was carried out.

A significant factor in this latest growth is those women aged 25-34, where a rise over 1995 of 40% has occurred, to 23.6% of women in this age band who no longer eat red meat, nearly 7 times the 1984 level.

Recent surveys have shown the dramatic decline in meat consumption amongst 16-24-year-old women, and this survey shows that this group is continuing to reject red meat as they age and influence the diet of their own families.

Since the 1995 survey over 1/2 million people have moved to a completely vegetarian diet, equating to 5,000 new vegetarians every week for the last 2 years.

The number of vegetarian women has only grown by 12%, so unlike in previous surveys, it is the men who have led the way with a 37% increase.

An all-time high of 46% of the population are now actively reducing their consumption of meat, and in particular red meat.

Whereas the principle reason for this change in recent surveys has tended to be 'health' concerns, a new trend has appeared in this survey.

'Financial' and 'moral' reasons have continued to decline in importance, and a new motivation, 'taste', has shown a significant change.

Compared with a figure of 16% in the 1995 survey, a record 24% have cited this as their primary reason for eating less meat.

This would perhaps suggest that consumers are 'going off' meat, and are moving more towards a pasta, cereal and vegetable-based diet.

BSE is another major factor, with nearly 22% citing it as their primary health concern, ahead of saturated fats, modern farming methods and existing health problems. Cholesterol remains the primary health concern.

• The above is an extract from the press release of the Realeat Survey 1984 – 1997, *Changing Attitudes to Meat Consumption* conducted by the Gallup Organisation.

© The Realeat Survey Office

Meat consumption

What has been the effect of vegetarianism and health scares on meat consumption?

Meat consumption is not declining, in fact MLC estimates show that total consumption has increased during the last 20 years. However, the market shares of the various meats are changing. Poultry meat has increased its market share over the period due to a considerable price advantage and it being perceived as a healthy option. During the 1970s poultry meat accounted for 18-20 per cent of the meat market. This had risen to around 39 per cent in 1996. So while consumption of the red meats has fallen, total meat consumption has been maintained. In 1976 total meat consumption was 3.64 million tonnes and in 1996, 4.14 million tonnes.

There is no evidence that vegetarianism is increasing. Currently just three per cent of the population claim to be vegetarian according to National Health Survey research. This has not changed over a number of years.

BSE scares have affected household consumption of beef. Following the initial scare in 1990 beef sales in GB fell by 25 per cent. By the end of that year sales had recovered to their previous levels. Following the latest scare purchases have fallen again. During 1996 sales fell by 16 per cent.

Supply has had a significant impact on the consumption of all the red meats in recent years:
• falling production for beef and lamb (high live exports are a contributing factor).
• devaluation of sterling made exports more competitive and significantly increased export volumes.
• higher exports had allowed intervention stocks of beef to be run down (the so-called beef mountain).
• devaluation of sterling made imports more expensive and resulted in a decline in imported supplies.

© Meat and Livestock Commission (MLC)

Vegetarianism

Only a few years ago if you became vegetarian you were considered a bit of a crank, but these days things have changed. There are already about 3 million vegetarians in this country and the number is increasing all the time. So why are so many people deciding to 'go veggie'?

Is eating meat cruel?...

Most people give up meat because they are concerned about the suffering involved. In Britain every year 750 million animals are killed for food. The vast majority of these animals spend their desperately short lives enclosed in horrible, squalid factory farms. Most pigs, chickens and turkeys are kept inside dark sheds without fresh air or daylight. Animals are often confined in cages so they cannot move about properly and many die from diseases caused by their overcrowded, unhealthy conditions.

Many chickens, pigs, sheep and cattle suffer even more pain and distress when they are transported to and from the market or slaughter-house. Crammed into lorries so tightly that they can hardly move and transported for hundreds of miles without food or water, many unfortunate animals don't survive the journey. It is often claimed that food animals are killed humanely, but there is no such thing as 'humane slaughter'.

According to the law, animals must be stunned so that they are unconscious when their throats are cut. In practice, however, stunning methods don't always work and many animals are conscious when they are killed. In the slaughterhouse, for example, poultry are hung upside down by their feet on a moving conveyer belt. Their heads are immersed in an electrically charged water bath to stun them before their throats are cut. They are then tumbled in boiling water to loosen their feathers. If the birds are not stunned properly and miss the automatic knife, they can end up being boiled alive!

So what is a vegetarian?

To put it simply, vegetarians are people who don't eat the flesh of dead animals. They avoid all forms of meat including poultry, fish and slaughterhouse products like animal fats and gelatine, although they do eat eggs and dairy products such as milk, yoghurt and cheese. People who also avoid eating eggs, dairy products and honey are called vegans.

...unnecessary?...

Meat is not needed for a healthy balanced diet. All the protein, carbo-hydrates, fats, minerals, vitamins, and fibre you need are provided by a balanced vegetarian diet. For example, there is more than enough protein in foods like beans, rice and nuts and vegetarians obtain minerals such as calcium and iron from leafy green vegetables, nuts and seeds. Most people who eat meat don't in fact eat a very healthy diet because they don't eat enough vegetarian food such as fresh fruit and vegetables. Nutritionists are always telling people that for good health they

should be cutting down on animal products and fats and eating a lot more fruit and vegetables.

unhealthy?...

Far from being essential for a healthy diet, it has now been shown that eating too much meat is bad for you, because it contains lots of saturated fats (which are not good for you) and no fibre (fibre is good for you). A good vegetarian diet is naturally low in fat and high in fibre and vitamins. Studies have shown that vegetarians are less likely to die of heart disease or to develop certain cancers. Vegetarians are also less likely to suffer food poisoning – 90% of food poisoning cases are related to animal products. BSE (Mad Cow Disease) is another worry.

Some scientists believe there's a chance that the disease could be passed on to people who eat infected beef.

Is meat wasteful and damaging the environment?...

Animal farming is a major source of pollution and environmental destruction. In this country intensive factory farming causes widespread water pollution; abroad, cattle ranching is responsible for destroying much of the tropical rainforest. Of the 150 acres of rainforest that are destroyed every minute it has been estimated that half is caused by livestock farming. In Central America alone 90% of the forest has been cleared primarily for cattle ranching.

Many of the world's fish populations have declined dramatically because of over-fishing. For example, it is estimated that a quarter of the entire fish population of the North

Sea is removed every year. Many sea bird populations have also shrunk because of the falling numbers of fish.

Rearing animals in order to eat them is a wasteful way of producing food. Livestock farming wastes the world's food resources because it uses land to grow crops to feed animals which are then killed for meat instead of growing crops that could feed far more people if fed directly on a vegetarian diet. In fact, only by cutting back on global meat consumption can we possibly provide enough food to feed the world.

Going veggie – the first steps

If you'd like to go veggie, but are not sure how – don't panic!

- Not everyone goes completely veggie straight away. Many people gradually cut down on the amount of meat they eat over several months, even years.

- Why not start off by giving up red meat and then gradually cutting out poultry and fish? Or you could try going without meat and fish for one day a week and then for two days a week and so on, gradually increasing the number of 'veggie days'.

- If the rest of your family still eats meat, don't worry. Find some ready-prepared veggie burgers, pies, pasties or pizzas that you can heat up and have instead of their meat versions. There are heaps of veggie foods in supermarkets these days and lots of easy-to-follow veggie cookbooks, too.

- Try experimenting with different foods and recipes to see what you like. Have a go at cooking some simple things yourself – you'll find ideas in our *Youth Group Recipe Booklet* – or try adapting your favourite meals into veggie versions. Once you start cooking vegetarian food you'll realise that there is a whole new world of food out there just waiting to be discovered.

Silly things people say

If you decide to go veggie then you're bound to get some hassle. Here are a few hints to help you deal with some of the sillier things that people say about going veggie.

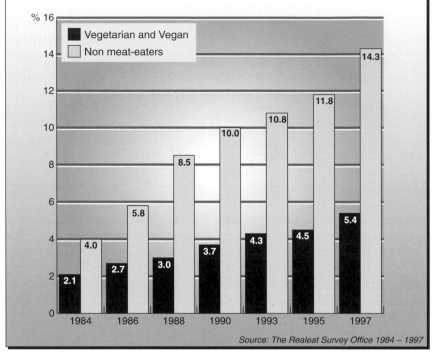

The growth in non meat-eating

The research for the survey has been carried out for Realeat by the Gallup Organisation. This year a total of 4,020 interviews were conducted. The sample aged 16 and over was representative of the population of Great Britain. The survey was conducted between 5th March and 18th March 1997.

Legend: Vegetarian and Vegan / Non meat-eaters

Year	Vegetarian and Vegan	Non meat-eaters
1984	2.1	4.0
1986	2.7	5.8
1988	3.0	8.5
1990	3.7	10.0
1993	4.3	10.8
1995	4.5	11.8
1997	5.4	14.3

Source: The Realeat Survey Office 1984 – 1997

Some silly things parents say:
In answer to: 'But you need to eat meat to stay healthy and fit.' Tell them: 'Actually by eating a balanced vegetarian diet I will probably be healthier than if I ate meat.' (Read the 'is meat unnecessary?' section)

In answer to: 'I don't have enough time to cook two meals. Besides, I don't know what to cook.' Tell them: 'You don't have to cook two separate meals. We can adjust the same meal to suit me too. We can replace the burgers, sausages, pies and pizzas with vegetarian versions; I can have nut roast instead of Sunday roast; cashew nut risotto instead of chicken risotto and so on. It won't be too hard to make 2 versions of the same meals and I'll help with the cooking.' (Especially when I get a copy of Animal Aid's recipe booklet!)

Some silly things friends say:
In answer to: 'It's perfectly natural for humans to eat meat.' Tell them: 'There's nothing natural about the way meat is produced today on factory farms and in slaughterhouses. And humans are omnivores, not carnivores; we can choose whether to eat meat or not.'

In answer to: 'You're just a hypocrite! You probably eat fish and wear leather shoes.' Tell them: 'At least I'm doing something, which feels a lot better than doing nothing.'

In answer to; 'Won't you get bored just eating vegetarian food?' Tell them: 'You've obviously never tried proper vegetarian food. Compared to an interesting vegetarian meal, a meat dish is "dead" boring!'

Helpful books for new veggies

A Vegetarian In The Family by Janet Hunt, published by Thorsons.
The Teenage Veggie Survival Guide by Anouchka Grose, published by Red Fox.

- Write to Animal Aid if you would like information on vegetarianism or if you have any questions that you'd like to ask them about going veggie. They have their own *Youth Group Recipe Booklet* which contains loads of delicious and easy to cook meal ideas sent in by members. To order your copy from Animal Aid, enclosing 75p and an A5-sized SAE, see page 41 for address details.

© Animal Aid
January, 1998

Wrecking the planet

Information from Animal Aid

'In environmental terms, meat-eating is a costly habit. The world's livestock herds consume increasing quantities of land, energy, and water. A quarter of the earth's landmass is used as pasture for livestock; more than half the farmland in the USA is devoted to beef production. While it takes, on average, 25 gallons (113 litres) of water to produce a pound of wheat in modern Western farming systems, it requires an astonishing 2,500 gallons (11,250 litres) of water to produce a pound of meat. Throughout the world, livestock herds accelerate erosion and desertification; 85% of topsoil loss in the USA is attributed to livestock ranching, for example.'

Joni Seager, *The State of The Environment Atlas,* Penguin Books, 1995

Livestock farming wrecks the world's natural resources. Did you know that:

- An estimated 100 million tonnes of methane (12-15% of all methane emissions) are released into the atmosphere each year by cattle, contributing significantly to global warming.

- According to David Gee, former Director of Friends of the Earth, meat is a terrible consumer of resources and a significant cause of global warming. He believes that the amount of carbon dioxide released into the atmosphere from the production of each pound of steak is equivalent to driving 25 miles in a car.

- Livestock farming is also a major source of rainforest destruction. Forests are cleared so that cattle can be grazed to produce beef-burgers. Eventually, grazing destroys the fertility of the soil and the cattle are moved on to yet more cleared forest. This process is known as 'hamburgerisation'.

- Vegetarians need less than a third as much water to sustain their diet as meat eaters do – an important advantage in a world increasingly concerned by shortages.

- Livestock farming is one of the biggest sources of water pollution. The *Meat Trades Journal* itself has stated that, in the UK, 'the list of companies which have been prosecuted by the National Rivers Authority for pollution offences reads like a Who's Who of the meat and food industry'.

Eat less meat and feed the world

'In cycling our grain through livestock, we waste 90% of its protein and 96% of its calories. An acre of cereal can produce five times more protein than an acre devoted to meat production; and legumes (beans, lentils, peas) can produce ten times as much. Thus the greater the

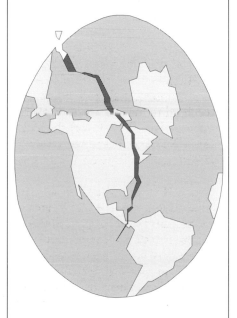

human consumption of animal products, the fewer people can be fed'

Joni Seager, *The State of the Environment Atlas,* Penguin Books, 1995.

One of the less well-known advantages of a vegetarian diet is that it is the most efficient way of producing food. With the human population still growing rapidly it has become vital that we eat less meat, because only by doing so will it be possible to feed far more people.

All the protein we eat is vegetable in origin. Our choice is whether to eat crops grown directly for human consumption or grow crops to feed to animals whom we eat after they have been fattened. The latter method is wasteful because animals – like us – use up most of their food's protein and energy value in the day-to-day workings of their bodies. By the time they are slaughtered most of the original food value has been lost.

When we eat meat we consume only 10% to 25% of the protein and energy value of crops that we would have obtained had they not been fed to animals first.

According to the influential Worldwatch Institute in the USA, 'those who consume livestock products and fish are competing directly with those who need grain for food'. The message from Worldwatch President, Lester Brown, is clear: 'Eat less meat and save the world.'

• The above is an extract from *Recipe for Life,* produced by Animal Aid in conjuction with The Vegetarian Campaign Group to promote the vegetarian diet. See page 41 for Animal Aids' address details.

© *Animal Aid* *January, 1998*

Free-range chickens and the hypocrisy of being vegetarian

As Marks & Spencer stop selling battery laid eggs. By James Erlichman

OK, I admit it – I'm a carnivore. I eat meat, and I eat it with intense pleasure. Lamb or pork, chicken or game, I love it all.

For years, however, I admired the self-restraint of vegetarians, the dedication to their cause which led them to pass up the delights of a succulent chop or a good roast. But no longer.

Now, having investigated animal welfare, I find it very hard to swallow the claims of all those millions of self-righteous vegetarians who say they care deeply about the protection of farm animals.

Only yesterday another vegetarian milestone appeared to be reached when Marks & Spencer announced it was banishing eggs laid by caged hens from its stores. From now on, it says it will sell only eggs laid by 'free-range hens'.

You might think this is a triumph for the animal welfare lobby. But the truth is that the EU rules governing free-range hens are a joke. Sure, the hens are not in a cage – but they are hardly free.

The rules allow them to be shoved into sheds of unlimited size, with no more space per bird than battery hens – about the size of this page. They have little holes by which they can leave the barn, but many don't, because they fear being pecked by dominant hens on the way back in.

M&S says its own rules are better than the EU minimum. But without being too cynical, it is a general rule in the egg trade that the best profits can be made from free-range eggs because welfare-conscious customers tend to be affluent and willing to pay over the odds to salve their consciences.

So while people celebrate the growing success of the animal welfare lobby and, coincidentally, the 150th anniversary of the Vegetarian Society, I have become convinced that they are deluding themselves.

We have turned our back on nature and have learned to pack farm animals into cages and sheds to slash the cost of production. The result is cheap bangers, burgers and chicken for the majority who eat meat

---

The stark truth is that they are often more cruel, and less honest, than meat-eaters. Notions such as 'free-range' are not the only delusions these people weave for themselves.

Outrageous, you say? Not a bit of it. More than a decade ago, when I was environment correspondent on a national newspaper, I was asked to write a book which forced me to look clearly at what really goes on behind the closed farm gates in intensive farming.

Since then I've spent much of my time writing and broadcasting on the unsavoury aspects of the food industry. Livestock are bred and raised cynically to produce animal products for us to eat. That's been happening for centuries.

But things have changed. We have turned our back on nature and have learned to pack farm animals into cages and sheds to slash the cost of production. The result is cheap bangers, burgers and chicken for the majority who eat meat.

At the same time, a tiny minority has also learned how to eat deliciously and nutritiously while avoiding animal products altogether – the vegans.

But let's turn to the group I now call the 'vicious veggies'. In what way, exactly, are they vegetarians?

IS THIS A LIFE SENTENCE OR DO WE GET REMISSION FOR GOOD BEHAVIOUR?

For what is 'vegetable' about milk, yoghurt, butter or cheese? These are animal products. And what is 'vegetable' about eggs? Aren't eggs unfertilised, expectant chicken foetuses?

This didn't even stop the pioneers of vegetarianism, who also had no qualms about dairy products. As one of its current members has admitted, the Vegetarian Society's original recipes were full of eggs and cream, with hardly any vegetables.

The religious basis for vegetarianism was reverence for all life. Cruelty to farm animals, then as now, is all about suffering – how much animals suffer, and for how long.

These days, the standard broiler chicken lives a very nasty life stuffed into a windowless barn for virtually the whole time. But it lives, on average, just 42 days from hatching to slaughter, so it is put out of its misery very quickly.

Contrast this with the suffering of laying hens that provide the eggs which over 90 per cent of vegetarians eat regularly. Most laying hens live imprisoned for up to two years in battery cages producing a vast number of eggs at an unnatural rate. People who base their diet on eggs can hardly be proud of this.

Chickens we must eat, by definition, reach the slaughterhouse in reasonable shape or we wouldn't want to eat them.

But death is different for the spent laying hen, scrawny and worth little after being exhausted with egg laying. Few are eaten whole any more so they needn't be protected from bruising or broken legs. They end up disguised in pies, soups and ready-made meals.

I accept my cruel role in all this So, why shouldn't egg-eating vegetarians, who have so happily dined off her for so long, also share the shame?

The intensive dairy industry is run along similar lines. I personally don't eat beef because of BSE, but let's consider the moral consequences of eating a fine sirloin steak. A discerning beef eater will have chosen meat that has come from a beef suckler herd where calves are allowed to stay with and suckle their

Market share

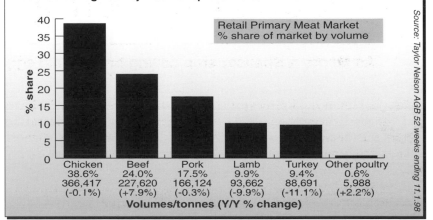

During 1997, chicken increased its volume share of the retail primary meat market from 38.5% to 38.6%. Beef has started to show signs of recovery and has increased its share by 1.9% to reach 24%. The lamb share also declined during 1997 by 1.0% to represent 9.9% of the market.

Retail Primary Meat Market
% share of market by volume

	Chicken	Beef	Pork	Lamb	Turkey	Other poultry
	38.6%	24.0%	17.5%	9.9%	9.4%	0.6%
	366,417	227,620	166,124	93,662	88,691	5,988
	(-0.1%)	(+7.9%)	(-0.3%)	(-9.9%)	(-11.1%)	(+2.2%)

Volumes/tonnes (Y/Y % change)

Source: Taylor Nelson AGB 52 weeks ending 11.1.98

mothers, grazing outdoors in a relatively natural way.

But most of our beef does not come from these fine suckler herds: few people realise that it actually comes from dairy cows.

Daisy is not only an amazing milk machine – producing more than 10,000 pints a year. She is also a meat machine.

To keep lactating she is kept constantly in calf. Most of the time she is impregnated with beef bull semen. This way the resulting calf will be 'beefy' enough to end up as meat you find in the supermarket.

The dairy calf isn't allowed to stay with its mother and is wrenched from her within a week to be raised in 'orphan herds'. The mother is milked until her yield drops, then it's time for the chop.

But before she goes she may be impregnated one last time – but this time with pure dairy bull semen in the hope of creating another milk machine.

If the resulting calf is female – great, another hard-working dairy cow is born. But if it's a male, it is useless either for milk or for meat because it was bred for an udder, not for prime beef steaks. And so it becomes one of those dewy-eyed veal calves for which vegetarians, in particular, wept so copiously when they were exported in veal crates to Holland.

Aren't all users of dairy products, and those vegetarians who generally eat more of them, guilty? And now that veal exports have been blocked

by the BSE beef ban, these infant male dairy calves are being slaughtered in Britain days after they're born. Can vegetarians really expect to escape blame for that, too?

In my view, true vegetarians are saints. These are the vegans who refuse to eat any animal products.

The number of vegans is small, but their cause and clarity of purpose is just. Nevertheless, even they benefit from animals because the vegetables they eat, particularly if they're organically grown, are fertilised with animal manure.

The truth is that meat eaters and vegetarians alike are too separated from farm production. Generations ago most of our ancestors lived and worked on the land. Even our grandparents still killed animals, or at least saw them whole, as carcasses in the local butcher.

But now farming has become intensive and brutal and, with our tacit permission, it has been hidden from us. Many of us eat only take-aways and ready-made meals. The closest most of us get to its realities is a slab of steak, a tub of yoghurt or an egg sandwich packed in plastic.

Today's conventional vegetarians would be on safer moral ground if they gave up dairy products and eggs and ate their pets instead. At least they would know then that the animal products they consumed had been well cared for before being put to a gentle death.

© *The Daily Mail*
October, 1997

Animal welfare

Animal welfare in beef, sheep and pig production.
Information from the Meat and Livestock Commission

Animal welfare is a very large and complicated subject, of great concern to a great many people, including the vast majority of livestock producers. Standards in the UK are good, but improvements must always be made. Even where we all agree that improvements are needed, however, it is not always clear what they should be and how they should be brought about, not just in this country but in Europe as a whole and beyond.

Improvement is continually taking place but rapid progress depends upon all of us working towards the same end. This article is intended to help inform this important debate.

What is animal welfare?

Cruelty to animals is against the law in this country, but 'positive' animal welfare goes far beyond the mere absence of cruelty.

It can be defined in general terms (e.g. physical or mental 'well-being') but translating it into better practice requires very detailed specifications related to the species of animal, its size, weight, age and sex. How an animal should be treated has to take all these things into account.

One also needs to ask who should define it animal welfare, because a plethora of different definitions will not help and most people will not accept a definition produced by what they see as 'interested parties'. It is vital that we do not simply bandy opinions about as to what is good for an animal, After all, lots of people think feeding toffees to a dog is good welfare.

Fortunately, in Great Britain we have a government-appointed but wholly independent body (Farm Animal Welfare Council – FAWC) set up to advise on Ministers and to arrive at a consensus on generally-acceptable definitions and standards. If we did not have it already, we would need to invent it.

An example of an improvement brought about in the UK, following a FAWC Recommendation, is the effective banning (in 1990) of narrow crates for the rearing of veal calves.

Of course, we do not all have to agree with the FAWC's conclusions and we must be able to argue about how they could be improved, but we do have to accept that they are the best effort at reaching a consensus view arrived at by a very wide range of people discussing all the evidence, from research and from practical experience.

FAWC defines positive welfare in terms of the conditions under which farm animals should be kept in order to satisfy the Five Freedoms: these are widely accepted as indicating the direction in which we should move. Strictly speaking, 100% achievement would not even be desirable. For example, is an animal never got thirsty it would

> ### The 5 Freedoms
> **1. Freedom from hunger and thirst**
> - by ready access to fresh water and a diet to maintain full health and vigour.
>
> **2. Freedom from discomfort**
> - by providing an appropriate environment including shelter and a comfortable resting area
>
> **3. Freedom from pain, injury or disease**
> - by prevention or rapid diagnosis and treatment.
>
> **4. Freedom to express normal behaviour**
> - by providing sufficient space, proper facilities and company of the animal's own kind
>
> **5. Freedom from fear and distress**
> - by ensuring conditions and treatment which avoid mental suffering.

never drink: and total absence of fear would lead an animal (as it would us) into danger. If it never experienced hunger, it would not eat and, as you can see with obese people, it is also possible to eat and drink too much.

For most farm animals, it is Freedom Number 4 (freedom to express normal behaviour) that raises most problems, because it implies considerable space and freedom. The first is costly and the second may lead to bullying, for example, since animals do not necessarily behave well towards each other when given total freedom – any more than humans do. Animals need space to avoid each other whilst they are establishing a pecking order (literally) and, by its very nature, farming cannot always allow enough space for this.

Many people like to think animals being kept under 'natural' conditions but, of course, farming itself is not 'natural'.

What is 'natural'

In nature animals eat each other and many die painfully of disease. They suffer injuries that get infected and all animals suffer from parasites, on the outside and on the inside. So did people in times past: fleas were 'natural' and so are dreadful parasites still in many parts of the world.

The fact is that we do not live 'natural' lives and would not want to. We no longer want to have fleas and we don't want them on our pets either.

So our responsibility to our farm animals includes preventing disease and controlling parasites, feeding them properly and protecting then from predators – all unnatural.

Nevertheless, we all instinctively feel that some practices are so unnatural that we object to them. Many people feel like that about excessive growth rates or milk yields and we need to think clearly about why we object and how to distinguish between these different sorts of unnatural features.

Why does animal welfare matter?

Some people believe that all sentient animals have rights but it is hard to see how the rights of the tiger and its prey can be protected simultaneously.

The reason they we refer to sentient animals is that they are judged to be capable of experiencing pain; not exactly as we do (we cannot, of course, know this anyway, and people differ greatly in their susceptibility to pain) but still capable of suffering.

And it is unnecessary or avoidable suffering that most people are against. Animals such as insects, slugs and worms (in general, the invertebrates) are considered non-sentient – which is just as well since it would be hard to avoid injuring them.

Indeed, we tend to take a different view of what we call vermin and pests, even if they are vertebrates and can feel pain.

Most people are more concerned about furry and feathered animals than they are about snakes and toads: we are not so sympathetic to ugly or dangerous animals even if they are furry!

But the main problem with the idea of animals having rights is that we cannot do anything sensible about them. Owls live on mice and voles: what does it say that both the owl and the mice have rights? And what are we going to do about it?

A more practical approach – with the same end result – is to accept that whenever we keep animals (or even affect them by our actions), we acquire a responsibility for their welfare because it is morally right to do so.

However, just how strongly people feel about this varies between individuals and between countries. It is well known that there are cultural differences between the dog-loving UK and the far-eastern countries where dogs are eaten and often cruelly treated. Cruelty to dogs also occurs here but it is not generally regarded as acceptable.

Recently, the cruel treatment of bears in parts of Asia (simply using

them to obtain their bile, for its apparent medicinal benefits) is an example of what would not be tolerated here. Many people object to bull-fighting – quite widely accepted in Spain and Portugal: but dog-fighting, cock-fighting and badger-baiting occur in this country even though they are illegal.

It is often held in this country we are more concerned than almost anywhere else. This has some foundation in fact but there is a great deal of cruelty to pets in this country, including the treatment of dogs when they have ceased to be the cuddly puppies given as Christmas presents, for example. However, this problem is decreasing. For example, it is reported that the RSPCA rescued 120,000 dogs in 1987 but this was down to 40,000 in 1994. Even so, the Wood Green Animal Shelter at Huntingdon still takes in some 7,000 unwanted dogs a year: so there is no room for complacency.

There tends to be more attention paid to how farm animals are kept – although most people eat them and would rather no think about the question of slaughter at all – partly because the numbers involved are so great but also because they are kept by other people. (The number of people actually involved in livestock production is a very small proportion of the population – probably less than 1%.) It is not

surprising that many farmers feel that they are picked on because they are easy targets.

Also, the image that the majority have of farming and the countryside tends to be romantic rather than realistic: thus outdoor rearing of animals seems to sound better even when we ourselves would far rather be indoors for most of the year (and most of each day).

However, just because there are welfare problems with horses, dogs, cats, hamsters, rabbits and a host of other companion animals, this does not mean that the welfare of farm animals is any less important.

Attitudes to welfare vary not only between people and cultures but also evolve over time, and at different rates in different places. Thus society no longer tolerates bear-baiting but has not entirely abandoned blood sports: that standards demanded by society thus change. Most of us would rather live in a society that cared about animals than in one that did not and every citizen is entitled to contribute to the way society behaves.

• The above is an extract from *Animal Welfare in Beef, Sheep and Pig Production*, written by Professor Sir Colin Spedding, Chairman of The Farm Animal Welfare Council, produced by the Meat and Livestock Commission.

© Meat and Livestock Commission

The Farm Animal Welfare Council (FAWC)

The 23 members are appointed by the Minister of Agriculture, as individuals but in such a way as to ensure that all sectors of the industry and those concerned are represented. These sectors include: farmers, veterinarians, local authority enforcer, consumers, animal welfarists (i.e. active in campaigning organisations), academics.

The Council is funded by MAFF but is completely independent: it can – and does – study what it wishes and is free to publish its findings. It also responds to specific Ministerial requests for advice.

Its remit is as follows: *'to keep under review the welfare of farm animals on agricultural land, at market, in transit and at the place of slaughter, and to advise the Minister of Agriculture, Fisheries and Food and the Secretaries of State for Scotland and Wales of any legislative or other changes that may be necessary.'*

The role of the FAWC is thus:

1. To advise Ministers on farm animal welfare as a basis for Codes of Practice and Legislation.
2. To promote positive farm animal welfare, on the farm, at markets, during transport and slaughter.
3. To identify research and development needs, since we do not know enough in some cases to give authoritative advice.
4. To liaise with similar organisations in other EU countries.

Animal welfare

Information from the National Farmers' Union

Animal welfare standards in the UK and the level of compliance with requirements for livestock care are at least equal of any in Europe.

Legislation in all aspects of animal protection – rearing on farm, transport, marketing and slaughter – is supplemented by codes of practice and professional guidance to ensure the best possible, and most appropriate, treatment. Livestock keepers, and those who are closely involved with farm animals, know that unless animals are humanely treated, they will not thrive.

Consumers must be confident that the food they eat is produced to the highest possible standards of safety, and under regulated animal welfare conditions. This information answers the questions that we are most frequently asked about animal welfare.

Food safety questions and answers

Q. Do farmers care about the welfare of their animals?
A. If you doubt that farmers care about their animals, just ask any farmer who has helped at the birth of a calf or lamb how much they care. Keeping animals is a full-time, 24-hour-a-day operation and farmers work to ensure their animals receive the best possible nourishment, shelter and veterinary care. A livestock farmer makes his living from his animals. It is therefore in his best interests to make sure they are kept in peak condition with full attention paid to their feeding, watering, resting and exercise. A sick, suffering animal will cost more to feed, will not grow as quickly or produce as good quality meat, eggs or milk.

Animal health problems can make the food product less saleable if not unsafe. So, there are many reasons why farmers care about animal welfare.

Q. So why are some animals intensively reared?
A. Intensive rearing normally refers to conditions where livestock are kept in large herds which tend to be kept inside for most of the year. There are a number of reasons why they are kept like this. Over the last 30 or so years, consumer pressures for cheaper foodstuffs have prompted a move towards larger farm units supplying the food processing industry with bulk quantities of cheap, high quality milk, meat and eggs. Rearing these animals intensively in this way means that farmers can supply these quantities whilst maintaining health, hygiene and other welfare standards.

Q. What do farmers do to ensure adequate animal welfare?
A. Farmers know that farm animals are sentient beings in that they can,

for example, feel pain, fear and fatigue. For this reason, they are committed to the humane treatment of their animals and the belief that animals have the right to the basic five freedoms at every stage of their lives. These freedoms, updated by the independent Farm Animal Welfare Council, define ideal states rather than standards of acceptable welfare.

These are:
- Freedom from hunger and thirst
- Freedom from discomfort
- Freedom from pain, injury or disease
- Freedom to express normal behaviour
- Freedom from fear and distress

Q. Do animals prefer to live outside?
A. No, not necessarily. Research has shown that some animals prefer to be inside where the temperature is controlled, where food is brought to them, etc. Also keeping animals outside presents a range of challenges of its own. Keeping animals in

extensive outdoor systems or in organic conditions does not eliminate the incidence of infections or parasitic diseases. For example, a high number of cases of salmonella in eggs has been traced to free-range systems where wild birds have contaminated the water and feed.

Q. How do farmers treat illness in their animals?
A. Freedom from disease is a very important component of good animal welfare. To prevent or cure disease in their animals, farmers or their veterinary surgeons will give them medicines.

All medicines given to animals are subject to strict licensing procedures by independent scientific advisers to Governments to ensure that they work, that they are safe for the animals, and will not be harmful to the consumers of the meat, milk or eggs from the animals.

Failure to prevent or cure disease could have serious consequences not only for the well-being of the herd or flock, but also for the economic viability of the farm.

Q. Why is it necessary to transport live animals?
A. There will always be a need to transport farm animals, whether it be from farm to farm, farm to market or to an abattoir, either within the UK or further afield.

Since the UK is part of the European single market, the frontiers between the member countries have become irrelevant. This makes the distinction between 'domestic' and 'export' journeys a false one. For example, it may now be more financially rewarding to sell pigs to buyers in Germany. British farmers support uniform strict welfare rules being applied fairly on all EU member states.

YES, there are strict regulations which livestock hauliers must follow when transporting animals.

Q. Are there any sort of guidelines governing the welfare of animals whilst they are being transported?
A. The regulations cover vehicle standards, stocking densities, feeding, watering and rest intervals. Failure to comply can lead to hauliers losing their authorisation to transport animals. The UK's implementation and enforcement of these regulations is amongst the strictest in Europe.

© *National Farmers' Union*

British chicken facts

Information from the British Poultry Meat Federation Ltd

Legal protection and controls
The health and welfare of British chickens are well protected by existing EU directives and UK legislation and Codes of Practice covering rearing, handling, transport and processing.

UK regulations and Codes are made mainly under the Agriculture (Miscellaneous Provisions) Act 1968, the Animal Health Act 1981 and the European Communities Act 1972.

The Welfare of Livestock Regulations 1994 on the Prevention of Cruelty to Animals set out conditions which must apply to different systems of livestock farming. For 'intensive systems', the Regulations require the livestock to be thoroughly inspected every day by a stockman who has been instructed and is knowledgeable about all relevant welfare Codes of Practice. Codes cover specific health and welfare aspects, litter management, prevention of heat stress and rodent control. Appropriate measures must be taken to safeguard the welfare of the livestock if any problems arise. The Regulations also require all automatic equipment in houses to be inspected daily. Automatic ventilation systems must have an alarm and back-up equipment in the event of a power failure. State veterinary service inspectors are empowered to enter any farm without prior notice to farmers.

The Welfare of Animals during Transport Order 1994 and amending Orders protect animals, including chickens, during transport. It sets out maximum journey times and requires people who transport

animals to have the knowledge and training appropriate to the animals for which they are responsible. At present, journey plans are required for certain journeys and animal transport certificates for all others.

The Welfare of Animals (Slaughter or Killing) Regulations 1995 protect animals, including chickens, in processing plants. All licensed processing plants have an independent Official Veterinary Surgeon (OVS) appointed by the Government Meat Hygiene Service.

The OVS has legal responsibility for enforcing welfare legislation on a day-to-day basis. Virtually all chickens in the UK are processed in licensed processing plants, meeting full European Union welfare and hygiene requirements. In unlicensed premises welfare and hygiene are the responsibility of the local authority.

In the interests of providing customers with products from chickens which have been farmed responsibly, retailers also closely monitor the health and welfare of birds, by regularly inspecting farms and demanding strict welfare standards. Only healthy birds without injury are acceptable at the processing plant, so good welfare is in the farmer's commercial interest.

The overwhelming majority of British chicken is produced in intensive rearing systems. However this does not mean the birds are cruelly treated. Cruelty is illegal as well as morally unacceptable and most companies include an instant dismissal clause in employment contracts in the case of cruelty or mistreatment by their staff of the birds in their care.

In 1992 an independent advisory group, the Farm Animal Welfare Council (FAWC), undertook an in-depth study into the rearing of chickens and concluded that the industry was generally well run and that the conditions in which the birds were kept satisfied most of their requirements for good welfare. FAWC was concerned about the potential for overcrowding in chicken houses and the strength in the legs and joints of growing birds. Both matters are being successfully addressed by the industry.

How are chickens housed?

There is considerable confusion in the public's mind about the housing system in which chickens reared for meat are raised.

Broiler or table chicken breeds differ from layer hens which produce eating eggs and are farmed in a different way. Chickens are reared from one day old in large purpose-built chicken houses on deep litter, comprising wood shavings or chopped straw. Chickens are not kept in cages but are free to roam and forage throughout the house, eating and drinking as they wish. Chickens are not beak trimmed nor subject to any other surgical procedures.

What happens inside the chicken house?

Farm management is key to successful chicken farming – if chickens are not well cared for, they will not pro-duce quality meat for the consumer.

The health, welfare, growth and economic performance of a flock of chickens is determined by what happens inside the chicken house. The housing, equipment and feed are all designed to meet the birds' nutritional and environmental needs. The birds are presented with a nutritious diet, clean water, a comfortable temperature and fresh air, all of which benefit their welfare and performance. It is the farmers' responsibility to ensure that the right balance of conditions exist. There is no conflict between the birds' welfare and the farm's economic perform-ance in these respects.

Good stockmanship is essential. Farmers inspect the birds in the house every day, usually checking two or three times. They walk the entire length of the floor, up and down, covering all parts of the house, using their training and experience to pick out any chickens which require attention. Sick birds are either treated or humanely culled on the spot.

In each house, a daily record is kept of the environmental factors which affect the comfort and performance of the flock and also a count of any birds which are culled or die. These records may be inspected by the OVS.

In any event all flocks going to the processing plant must be accompanied by a production report to the OVS. This gives details of flock health including any veterinary medicines which may have been administered.

The number of birds which die during rearing has been reducing and is currently below five per cent. This is low by any agricultural standard, but chicken farmers are working to reduce mortality further. While some deaths are inevitable in any large population of animals or birds, chicken farmers do not consider any mortality as acceptable.

Strict farm hygiene procedures, including equipment cleaning and restrictions on visitors, are observed by the stockmen to protect the health and welfare of birds in their care.

How are chickens caught and transported to the processing plant?

British chicken farmers follow strict legislation and codes of practice on the catching and transport of chickens.

The proper handling of birds requires skill and catching is undertaken by trained and competent staff. It is carried out quietly and with care to avoid unnecessary struggling which could bruise or otherwise injure the birds.

Most companies have invested in modular drawer systems. Modules are placed inside the house close to the chickens being caught. Birds are carried upside down for a short distance and placed in the modules. The full module is then taken out of the house to the lorry.

Most chickens travel fewer than 50 miles from the farm to the processing plant. The birds are protected from extreme weather conditions by roofs on each module and side curtains on the lorry. On arrival, the birds are rested and inspected under the supervision of the Official Veterinary Surgeon.

Over 700 million chickens are transported every year. In any population of this size, deaths will inevitably occur. The rate of deaths during transport (known as dead-on-arrival) is one of the lowest of all farmed livestock, currently less than 0.2 per cent.

Nevertheless, the industry is working with research institutes and MAFF to design transport systems to reduce further the stress on chickens in transit and the rate of dead-on-arrival at the processing plant.

How are chickens processed?

At the processing plant the transport modules are unloaded from the lorries and the birds, still in the individual drawers, are moved a short distance by conveyor to the processing line. They are then hung by both shanks on specially designed shackles on a moving line. The shackles are carefully designed to support the weight of the birds without pinching their shanks. Subdued lighting is used during this process and the birds remain calm throughout.

Every step is taken to ensure that chickens are processed without distress or pain. As required by law, the birds are rendered unconscious and insensitive to pain in an electrical stunning waterbath and are immediately killed by cutting major blood vessels in the neck. Muscle

All the indications are that consumption of chicken meat in this country and throughout the world will continue to rise

tremor after neck cutting can sometimes be seen but this should not be mistaken for consciousness.

The stunning and slaughtering of birds is carried out only by licensed slaughtermen under the independent supervision of the OVS and qualified Poultry Meat Inspectors, who regularly monitor the stunning equipment and check the accuracy, effectiveness and duration of the stun.

The industry is co-operating in research into continuing improvements to electrical stunning and alternative methods.

What is selective breeding?

It is the breeding programmes, together with everyday stock management, which ensure the health and welfare of the UK chicken flock. Breeding companies produce chickens well suited to today's farming systems.

All chicken breeding procedures in the UK rely on natural mating and laying behaviour. All breeding stock are kept in environmentally controlled houses on litter.

Birds are selected to meet a number of criteria. They are chosen for the consistency of meat quality and feed efficiency, but equally important are welfare characteristics such as physiological (heart, lungs and other organs) and skeletal

British chicken farmers are not complacent and realise that improvements can and must continue to be made

strength to ensure a physically robust and healthy flock. Robust health is a prerequisite for the efficient production of quality meat.

Every bird in the primary breeding flocks is physically examined. Lixiscope technology is used for any defects in leg joints. Only birds displaying the required traits are kept for the breeding programme. Birds which have not been selected for breeding are reared as chickens for meat.

Selective breeding has eliminated several serious diseases from chicken breeding flocks in the UK. A reassessment of the selection criteria in the late 1980s has led to major reductions in leg disorders which are now negligible on well-managed chicken farms.

Breeding companies are developing the use of genetic information in their breeding programmes, but have no plans for undertaking invitro manipulation of the genetic material in chicken breeds.

The future of chicken farming in the UK

All the indications are that consumption of chicken meat in this country and throughout the world will continue to rise. It offers quality, versatility, health benefits and value for money to all households.

Farmers must therefore meet the demand for this popular product, whilst recognising the integral role good health and welfare has in providing top quality chicken.

Chicken farmers and processors receive no production or price supports under the European Union Common Agricultural Policy. The industry has never sheltered behind subsidies but responds quickly and effectively to the needs and concerns of the public.

British chicken farmers are not complacent and realise that improvements can and must continue to be made. They will maintain investment in training, research and up-to-date housing and equipment, meeting their responsibility to provide good conditions for the health and welfare of the birds in their care.

© *The British Poultry Meat Federation Ltd*

Laying hens

Farm facts from Compassion in World Farming Trust (CIWF)

Introduction

The ancestors of our modern hens are thought to be the red jungle fowl that live in the forests of India and South-East Asia. Domestic chickens first appeared in China around 1400 BC. Naturally, chickens would make a nest and lay one or two clutches of eggs a year which they would incubate. When the chicks hatched the hen would protect her young in their first few weeks of life. Today's modern egg-producing hen has a very different life.

How many laying hens are there in the UK?

There are around 34 million laying hens in the UK and around 30 million (88%) are kept in battery cages.

What are battery cages?

The cages have a sloping wire floor and measure 46cm x 51cm, very small when you realise that a hen's wingspan is about 80cm. Usually 5 birds are kept in a cage of this size – it's illegal to keep most birds in a cage where they cannot spread their wings out fully – but not for hens!

Where are the cages kept?

The cages are arranged in rows (or batteries) 3–6 tiers high inside huge, windowless sheds. Each shed can contain between 10,000 and 75,000 hens. Artificial light is kept on 17 hours a day to encourage hens to lay more eggs. (The conditions try to mimic summer.) Heating and ventilation is controlled. Feeding is automatic, the food being carried along a conveyor belt in front of the cages.

How can hens behave naturally in the cages?

The answer is they cannot carry out normal behaviours properly in these very cramped conditions. They are unable to scratch around in any kind of litter, dustbathe (fluffing up fathers in dry mud), peck at the earth or build a nest. They can of course eat, drink, pass waste and lay eggs. The birds cannot stretch their wings fully, walk, run or fly up to a perch.

How does living in a cage affect their behaviour?

Because they cannot behave normally some behaviours become altered. Instead of pecking at the ground they peck one another, remove feathers, peck at the flesh and cause wounds. In severe conditions the birds will even kill one another. Chicks are often de-beaked or beak-trimmed to stop them pecking one another. Beak-trimming is painful and the pain lasts through the birds' lives. The tip of the beak is usually removed with a red hot metal blade.

How old are the battery hens when they are put in the cages?

Hens are put into the cages when they are 18 weeks old, just before they start laying eggs. After about a year the hens lay fewer eggs. On most farms they will then be removed from the cages and be slaughtered, The tough meat is used in soup, paste and pet food.

How many eggs does a hen produce?

Modern hens have been bred to produce many more eggs than their

---

Broiler chickens

Introduction

Broiler chickens are the ones we rear especially for the meat we call 'chicken'. These birds have been especially bred over many years to grow quickly and put on weight (meat) quickly. We rear and kill 600 million broilers each year in the UK. Compassion in World Farming is very concerned about the welfare of broilers on modern intensive farms. The following questions and answers should help explain our concerns.

Where do broiler chickens live?

They live in huge sheds without windows or any form of natural light. The largest sheds can contain up to 100,000 birds but 10-20,000 is the norm. The birds do not live in cages, but are kept on the floor which is covered in a deep layer of 'litter' – usually wood shavings. Conditions become very cramped as the birds grow, each bird may have only 0.55 square feet of space – an area smaller than the cover of a telephone directory. The sheds are not cleaned out during the lifetime of the birds. The wood shavings become damp, greasy and very smelly.

The wet 'litter' contains ammonia from the chickens' waste. This can cause blisters to develop on the birds' breasts, ulcers on their feet and burns on their legs. These can all be very painful.

How are the chickens cared for?

It's impossible for so many birds to receive individual care. The birds are fed and given water automatically by machines. The person in charge simply has to maintain the equipment, check on the general health of the birds, removing those that die.

© Compassion in World Farming (CIWF)

wild ancestors, which laid around 20 in a year. Today's battery hens lay more than 250 eggs a year on average.

What happens to the male chicks?
Obviously the males do not lay eggs and they are not the right breed for meat. Around 234 million day-old male chicks are killed each year. They are either gassed with carbon dioxide gas or placed in a huge machine that minces them alive.

What are the alternatives to battery eggs?
These include semi-intensive systems known as percheries or aviaries and of course the free-range system.

What are percheries and aviaries?
In percheries and aviaries birds are kept in large sheds with several tiers or perches, plus floor space with litter (usually woodshaving or wood-shavings and straw). Nest boxes are provided and there may be natural light. The systems vary but some can still be very crowded. They are an improvement on the battery system. The eggs from these systems are sold as 'Barn Eggs'.

What is free-range?
Hens in this system may be kept in a large perchery-type shed but there must be an outside area covered in vegetation. Conditions can be very good for the birds if there are not too many birds and especially where a number of small moveable houses are used (each house holds around 100 birds). Free-range hens can behave naturally – scratch and peck at the ground , stretch and flap their wings, dustbathe etc. The eggs are sold as 'Free-Range Eggs'.

Why are there no egg boxes labelled 'Battery Eggs'?
Unfortunately, the government refuses to force battery egg producers to label their eggs showing just how they were produced. Battery eggs are often labelled 'Farm Fresh' or 'Country Fresh'. If you want to avoid battery eggs only buy those labelled 'Free Range'.

What does the law say about battery cages?
European law says a hen must have a minimum floor space of 450cm^2 – less than the size of this page. Many scientists and vets state that this causes a hen great suffering. A European scientific report has said the battery cage system should be phased out, but so far this has not been agreed by the European Agriculture Ministers.

© Compassion in World Farming (CIWF)

Why go vegetarian?

Vegetarians are very much like everyone else. They eat many of the same things as meat-eaters, shop in the same supermarkets (but spend less time in certain meaty aisles!), and even eat out in many of the same places

There was a time when being a vegetarian was seen as being quite weird, but the facts speak for themselves. What's so strange about wanting to eat healthy, fresh food that hasn't died for the dinner table?

Vegetarianism is good for the environment and doesn't cost the earth.

Factory farming
Story books show farms as cosy places where hens run around in the yard, pigs wallow in mud and lambs play in the fields. Unfortunately, reality isn't always like that. Most modern farms are more like factories and the animals are treated like food-producing machines.

Many animals are kept shut up in crowded sheds their whole life through. Some will have been changed by selective breeding and genetic engineering so that they grow faster, have more offspring, grow more wool or produce more milk than any animal would in the wild.

These changes don't benefit the animals – they just increase profits. Factory farms also deny animals their natural instincts. They cannot move around freely, care for their young or even choose their food.

Just imagine being locked in the school toilets with 30 or 40 other people for the rest of your life, with nothing to do – no television, games, or music and only porridge to eat.

Broiler brutality
There is no scratching around the farmyard for chickens on modern factory farms. Known as broilers, up to 100,000 birds are kept together in windowless sheds with dim electric lights. They are fed on a high protein diet and given antibiotics to help them grow faster so that by the time they are six or seven weeks old, the chickens are twice as heavy as they should be. This excess weight causes problems such as lameness, arthritis and even leg deformities.

The sheds are never cleaned out during the life of the chickens – the layer of droppings just gets higher and higher. Lots of birds die from disease and stress and rot where they fall.

At six or seven weeks old, the birds are rounded up and stuffed into crates. Some get their wings or legs broken at this stage. The crates are loaded onto lorries and driven to the slaughterhouse.

Assault and battery

Ninety per cent of the eggs you find in shops are laid by hens kept in battery cages. These wire cages usually house five birds and are so small that each bird has just about the same amount of space as this page. They can't stretch their wings, make a nest or take a dust bath and their feet become deformed from standing on the wire mesh all the time. Many have almost all their feathers plucked out by bored or aggressive cage mates. Some birds have their beaks sliced off with a hot wire or blade to stop this feather plucking. Wild hens would live for 12 years, but battery hens are worn out by the time they are two and sent for slaughter.

The pork on your fork

Pigs are as intelligent and sensitive as dogs, but most are sentenced to a life of boredom and misery. Wild pigs live in woodland areas and the sows like to build a nest of grass and leaves for their young. In factory farms they have to give birth in a narrow metal crate, where they can't turn round and can only move one step backwards or forwards.

The piglets are taken away from their mother when they are only three to four weeks old so the sow can be mated again. They are fattened up in overcrowded pens, and killed at five to seven months old to become pork, bacon and ham.

Luckless lambs

You can still see lambs skipping around in fields and so most people think that sheep don't have too bad a time. They don't realise what goes on behind the scenes. For example, four million lambs die every year within a few days of being born. Often the pregnant ewes are not fed well, or they are forced to have their lambs earlier in the year than would happen naturally. As the farmers try to save money, fewer shepherds now have to look after bigger and bigger flocks, and many lambs die of exposure on cold, lonely hilltops.

Beyond beef

There are different breeds of cows – some are kept for beef and some for milk.

A dairy cow must have a calf every year, otherwise her milk dries up. Her calf is usually taken away after only a few days, so that we can drink its milk. More calves are born than are needed in a dairy herd, so the unwanted ones are sent to livestock markets. Some will be fattened up as beef, but around 500,000 a year are sent overseas to veal crates which are banned in this country because they are so cruel.

Cows would naturally live for about 20 years, but are worn out after six or seven years in dairy herds and are slaughtered.

Killing with kindness?

Lots of people think that it's acceptable to eat meat because they have been told that animals in this country are killed humanely. A pistol with 15cm bolt is shot into the brain to stun the animal so that it feels no pain when its throat is being cut.

But the bolt has to hit the right spot exactly. If the animal moves its head as the pistol is fired, it could end up painfully wounded but fully conscious. One RSPCA report showed that up to half of all young bulls may suffer terrible pain as the stun gun fails to hit the target.

Smaller animals are stunned with electric shocks, and poultry are dunked head first into an electrically-charged water bath. Many birds don't hang meekly on the conveyor belt, but move around trying to escape. Some move at the wrong time, missing both the stunning bath and the knife. They end up being plunged alive into a scalding tank designed to loosen their feathers after death.

• The above is an extract from *Food for Life*, produced by Animal Aid and the Vegetarian Society.

© *Animal Aid and the Vegetarian Society*

The RSPCA's welfare standards for farm animals

The welfare standards cover aspects of farm animal care that might influence animal health, comfort and contentment. Some key issues covered in the standards:

Philosophy

The standards aim to provide a wholesome diet, fed in appropriate quantities which are readily accessible, together with an environment that provides plenty of space for exercise, normal behaviour and interaction with other animals. Focusing on safety, hygiene and comfort – the standards aim to ensure a happier, healthier animal.

Food and water

The standards specify that the food must be appropriate to the species. It should provide adequate nutrition and be easily accessible to avoid bullying. Feed must be safe and hygienically stored to avoid contamination.

• No growth-promoting hormones are permitted.

• Mammalian proteins are not permitted.

• Antibiotics may only be administered on veterinary advice.

• Water must be fresh, plentiful and access is specified.

Environment

Animals must be provided with a well-drained, clean and well-bedded lying area, providing comfort and hygiene. Animals should have protection from predators such as foxes. The environment must be enriched to create more satisfying, rewarding and animal-friendly farming systems.

Space

Increased space allowances are stipulated to ensure animals have sufficient space to move around, lie down and interact with company of their own kind. Stalls and tethers for sows and battery cages for hens which restrict movement, natural behaviour and interaction are not acceptable.

Health

A health plan must be written establishing preventative measures to avoid disease, plus plans to deal with existing ailments. Any medication given to any animal for any illness and any animal losses must be recorded. A sick pen must be provided for any injured or sick animals.

Transport

- Staff must be trained in animal handling to ensure all animals are handled sympathetically, thus reducing stress and injury, particularly during loading and unloading.
- The inside of the vehicle must be safe, hygienic and inviting through proper ventilation and lighting. Good footing should be in place, both inside the vehicle and on any ramps, to avoid slips and falls.
- Steep ramps should be avoided to ensure ease of access and reduce accidents.
- Space allowances are specified to avoid injury and stress from overcrowding and avoid animals falling due to being given too much space.
- Maximum transportation times are specified – and never more than 8 hours.

Slaughter

- A trained Animal Welfare Officer must be appointed at the abattoir to supervise and instruct all employees required to handle live animals thus ensuring animals are handled sympathetically.

- The lairage and abattoir must be designed to ensure stress and risk of injury is minimised and to encourage animals to move forward calmly without resistance.

Summary of the RSPCA welfare standards by species

Note: the welfare standards cover the whole of the animal's life – at the farm, during transit and at the abattoir.

Laying hen standards
- The RSPCA welfare standards exclude caged hens
- Specify increased space allowances over minimum legal requirements
- Specify number of feeders and drinkers and accessibility
- Facilities must be provided for perching, nest boxes for nesting and laying eggs, litter for

scratching and dustbathing, all designed to provide a richer, more satisfying environment

For free-range systems
- Specify minimum size of pophole, to ensure all birds are encouraged to leave the house and range
- Specify requirements for shelter on the range to reduce stress and panic due to overhead threats and predators
- Birds must be inspected at least three times a day

Chicken standards
- Through the control of nutrient content and feeding, the growth rate is slowed down to avoid leg weakness and heart failure. Further reduction in leg weaknesses is delivered through increased space allowances, encouraging more movement and exercise.
- In-feed antibiotics may only be prescribed by a vet for specific diseases and not simply used to mask poor housing and management
- Producers are asked to improve the birds' environment to make it more interesting and satisfying
- The standards require that good air quality is maintained at all times through effective ventilation
- Good quality litter must be provided to reduce skin breast

infections and injuries, especially to feet and hock
- The birds must be inspected at least three times a day
- Catching and crating methods are specified to reduce injuries and stress
- All personnel handling the birds must be trained in animal welfare
- Transportation requirements are specified to reduce injury and stress
- Handling at the abattoir is specified to reduce stress and injury

Turkey standards
- Aim to reduce leg weaknesses and hip deformation which result in painful, debilitating lameness
- Increased space allowances over and above the legal recommendations to encourage exercise and exploration of the environment
- Provide a totally littered environment to encourage dustbathing
- Lighting must be sufficient to allow investigation and natural behaviour but not to result in fighting
- The standards require the environment to be enriched to reduce fighting and to provide for a more satisfying environment
- The birds must be inspected at least three times a day
- Catching and crating methods are specified to reduce injury and stress
- Personnel handling the animals must be trained in animal welfare
- Handling at the abattoir is specified to reduce stress and injury

Sheep standards
- Extra care is required around lambing time to minimise ewe/lamb trauma and death, thereby resulting in strong, healthy lambs
- Regular foot care in the form of footbaths, vaccination and trimming to reduce the incidence of lameness in breeding flocks
- Shelter at the critical times, especially on hill farms during winter

- Ensure that the rams' general health and welfare is not forgotten
- Require that both intestinal and skin parasites are properly controlled
- Health plan is in place to improve ewe and lamb survival through appropriate preventative measures and appropriate records

Pig standards
- Cover the whole of the animal's life from breeding farm, fattening farm, haulier and abattoir
- The RSPCA standards exclude stalls and tethers which restrict sows in close confinement pens
- Dry, comfortable straw bedding must be provided, for as well as offering more comfort, it also provides for a more interesting, less frustrating environment by the encouragement of foraging and rooting behaviour
- Specify increased space allowances over minimum legal requirements with more space to lie down in comfort, and more opportunity to exercise and explore

Outdoor pigs
- Appropriate climatic and soil conditions are vital when establishing outdoor units
- Provision of shelter, wallows, dips and sprinklers to avoid overheating and sunburn
- Specify number of feeders and drinkers and accessibility
- Goads are not allowed to be used at the abattoir

Beef cattle standards
- The RSPCA does not allow the keeping of cattle on totally slatted floors without access to comfortable bedding

- Require increased space allowances over the minimum legal requirements. There should be adequate space for exercise and for interaction with others
- A dry, comfortable bedded area must be provided
- Maintenance of healthy body condition throughout the year

Calves
- The RSPCA excludes veal crates and systems requiring calves to be closely confined in small pens for several months
- Calves must receive adequate levels of colostrum and first milk from their mother – vital for their long-term health and survival
- Strict hygiene is employed in the care and feeding of young calves
- Calves are kept in a group housing environment to encourage interaction with other calves
- Straw bedding must be provided to ensure a comfortable and interesting environment
- Sufficient nutrients and fibre must be provided to develop a normal digestive system, prevent anaemia and reduce digestive upsets

Dairy cattle standards
- A comfortable, well-drained lying area is required to encourage resting and thereby contribute to reducing foot problems
- Hygienic lying areas and clean walkways to keep feet in good condition, prevent soiling of the bed and help keep udders clean and hygienic
- Lameness prevention programme involving foot trimming, footbathing, appropriate diet and dry, hygienic conditions underfoot
- Increased space allowances to reduce bullying and stress and to allow for exercise whilst indoors over winter
- Strict hygiene conditions during the milking process to protect the cow from disease, ensure milk quality and to reduce infection of the udder (mastitis).

© RSPCA

Why vegan?

Information from Vegan Action

What is a vegan?

A vegan consumes and purchases products which do not come from animals.

Vegans avoid dairy products, eggs, and flesh; as well as leather, wool, honey and all products which contain slaughterhouse ingredients (many soaps and shampoos). Most vegans also avoid animal-tested products (cosmetics, herbicides, household cleaners). Although it may be impossible to eliminate all such products from one's life, vegans will usually do their best to find cruelty-free alternatives.

The term vegan was coined in London in 1944 by seven vegetarians who met to form the Vegan Society, which still thrives in England. Like vegans today, they were concerned with the ethical and health consequences of eating animal products, as well as with animal agriculture's destructive effects on the planet.

Benefit to animals

While some people might be conscious of what transpires in today's slaughterhouses, few are aware of the inherently cruel and exploitative nature of the dairy and egg industries.

Battery hens used for egg production are possibly the most ill-treated of all farm animals. Their entire lives are spent in cages so small that they cannot concurrently spread their wings. The cages, stacked three to four levels high, have wire mesh floors which are slanted to allow the eggs to roll onto a belt. Lacking solid ground to wear down their claws, the hens' feet often become permanently attached to the floors.

Amputation of the last digit of the hens' toes solves this problem. Egg producers have learned that along with minimising the light available to layers, searing or clipping off a large portion of the hens' upper mandible will reduce the damage done by frustrated birds suffering from stress-induced violence. These practices are performed without anaesthesia, resulting in the premature death of many hens. Even those who survive these procedures can expect to live only a year and a half, far less than the fifteen to twenty years of which they are capable.

Egg-farmers regularly lace the birds' food with antibiotics to lessen outbreaks of disease. Nevertheless, salmonellosis and leukosis are extremely common in flocks.

Dairy cows have also fallen victim to animal agriculture's demand to cut production costs. Thanks to the pharmaceutical industry, dairy farmers now have the option of utilising a wide array of growth hormones and drugs, including the genetically engineered rBGH, which has been linked to a variety of health problems. A steadily increasing number of dairy cows are being kept in confinement for their entire, abbreviated lives.

Those who do not have to exist in concrete stalls must still endure almost constant pregnancy (to ensure continual lactation) and immediate separation from their calves conceived through artificial insemination.

Calves, especially if male, are generally sold to the veal industry and will suffer through sixteen weeks of severe confinement before slaughter. After six to seven years (less than one-third of their possible life expectancy) in the dairy industry most cows are spent and will be sold for low-grade beef.

Environmental benefits

In the US and other nations, the impact animal agriculture has had on the environment has been devastating. Raising animals for food is a wasteful and inefficient process. Becoming a vegan translates into a drastic alleviation of the stress we place on our environment, as a plant-based diet requires far less water, energy, raw materials, and land to produce.

Feedlots and slaughterhouses in the US are the largest single polluters of rivers and streams. Furthermore, crops destined for animal feed are not required to meet the same standards as those grown for human consumption, resulting in chemical pesticides and herbicides being applied more liberally. These chemicals are passed on to consumers in their milk, eggs and meat.

Animal Damage Control, a government agency, annually kills millions of indigenous animals, from coyotes to crows, all at the behest of cattle and sheep ranchers, who also vehemently oppose the reintroduction of native species such as the wolf.

From the overuse of water to soil erosion and deforestation, it is difficult to overstate the case for re-examining what we eat.

Health benefits

Considering the horrors of the animal agriculture industry, it is comforting to know that a diet free from animal exploitation offers so many health benefits. An increasing number of studies are showing that human nutritional needs are best met with a vegan diet.

Dr T. Colin Campbell, a Cornell University nutritional biochemist, supervised the largest, most in-depth nutritional epidemiological study of its kind ever undertaken. The close observation of the eating habits of 6,500 Chinese participants over a seven-year period brought him to conclude that, 'We're basically a vegetarian species and should be eating a wide variety of plant foods and minimising our intake of animal foods.' He further stated, 'In the next ten years, one of the things you're bound to hear is that animal protein...is one of the most toxic nutrients of all that can be considered.' Indeed, a direct link was found in this study between the consumption of animal products and life-threatening illnesses such as heart disease and cancers of the breast and colon.

Not only do animal products pose health risks for human

Vegetarians and vegans, by sex

The research for the survey has been carried out for Realeat by the Gallup Organisation. This year a total of 4,020 interviews were conducted. The sample, aged 16 and over, was representative of the population of Great Britain. The survey was conducted between 5th March and 18th March 1997.

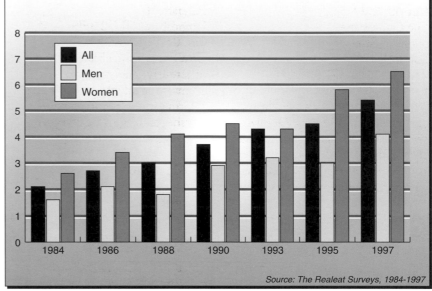

Source: The Realeat Surveys, 1984-1997

consumers, they offer us nothing nutritive that cannot be more readily obtained from plant sources. Protein, iron, calcium and all vitamin requirements are easily met through eating only grains, beans, vegetables, nuts and fruits, with the possible exception of vitamin B-12, which, if needed, is available in fortified foods and supplements.

While the question many people ask when comparing the vegan diet to a standard diet is 'Will I get enough?', it is much more important to ask 'Have I been getting too much?' While the fat content of a vegan diet is substantially lower than an omnivorous one, what might be equally beneficial is the lower protein intake. Excess animal protein has been linked to osteoporosis, kidney disease, and even cancer. Americans, it has been shown, typically have three to four times as much protein in their diet as is necessary.

Putting it into practice

Becoming vegan is easy. Many traditional American dishes, such as hot dogs and ice cream, now have their vegan equivalents. You may also want to look into the cuisines of other cultures such as Thai, Ethiopian, or Persian. If you live in a city there will probably be a wide selection of ethnic markets and

restaurants to choose from which offer vegan foods (ask about cooking oil or broths which might be of animal origin).

Non-leather shoes, belts and other accessories are easy to find. Many department stores sell canvas, rubber or vinyl shoes and belts. Health food stores carry a wide variety of vegan products such as soap, shampoo, and toothpaste, while many mainstream companies are catching on to this demand, resulting in the wider availability of vegan items in supermarkets and drugstores. Try cleaning your house with a simple cleaner like Murphy's Oil Soap or Bon Ami instead of big-name, toxic cleaners or find a book on making your own with simple household items such as vinegar and baking soda.

Your everyday actions effect all of the Earth's inhabitants. By learning to consume only what you need, you can, as the saying goes: 'Live simply so that others may simply live.' While making these changes can be difficult at first, you will eventually find that they become second nature.

If you believe in making a positive statement through your lifestyle we're sure you'll choose veganism!

© Vegan Action

ADDITIONAL RESOURCES

You might like to contact the following organisations for further information. Due to the increasing cost of postage, many organisations cannot respond to enquiries unless they receive a stamped, addressed envelope.

Animal Aid
The Old Chapel
Bradford Street
Tonbridge
Kent, TN9 1AW
Tel: 01732 364546
Produces information including their quarterly magazine *Outrage*. To receive information on an issue or for a list of educational and information resources, send a large s.a.e. to the address above.

British Chicken Information Service
Bury House
126-128 Cromwell Road
London, SW7 4ET
Tel: 0171 373 7757
Fax: 0171 373 3926
Produces an *All About Poultry* educational video. The video ties in very closely with the *All About Poultry* education pack which was launched in January 1998. For copies of the new video for schools use, please contact the Educational Project Resources Department.

British Nutrition Foundation (BNF)
High Holborn House
52-54 High Holborn
London, WC1V 6RQ
Tel: 0171 404 6504
An independent charity which provides reliable information and advice on nutrition and related health matters. They produce a wide range of leaflets, briefing papers and books.

British Poultry Meat Federation (BPMF)
Imperial House
15-19 Kingsway
London, WC2B 6UA
Tel: 0171 240 9889
Trade organisation representing producers within the UK.

Compassion in World Farming Trust (CIWF)
5a Charles Street

Petersfield
Hampshire, GU32 3EH
Tel: 01730 268070
CIWF seeks the abolition of inherently cruel practises to live animals for slaughter. Publishes information including a series of factsheets called *Farmfacts* on various issues.

Freedom Food
The Causeway
Horsham
West Sussex, RH12 1HG
Tel: 01403 264181
Fax: 01403 241048
Freedom Food aims to be the most credible and trustworthy animal welfare assurance scheme in the country, embracing RSPCA welfare standards that lead the way in farm animal welfare.

Meat and Livestock Commission
PO Box 44, Winterhill House
Snowdon Drive
Milton Keynes, MK6 1AX
Tel: 01908 677577
The Meat and Livestock Commission (MLC) supports the marketing of British meat and livestock, offers support to farmers and others in the meat and livestock industry, and promotes training and research in the meat industry.

National Farmers' Union (NFU)
164 Shaftesbury Avenue
London, WC2H 8HL
Tel: 0171 331 7200
Fax: 0171 331 7313
Represents farmers and growers in England and Wales.

Royal Society for the Prevention of Cruelty to Animals (RSPCA)
The Causeway
Horsham
West Sussex, RH12 1HG
Tel: 01403 264181
The RSPCA is the world's oldest animal welfare organisation. Produces publications.

The Food Commission
94 White Lion Street
London, N1 9PF
Tel: 0171 837 2250
Fax: 0171 837 1141
Provides education, information, advice and research on nutrition, diet, health and food production. Runs various educational and research campaigns, publishes *Food Magazine* and other publications.

The Vegan Society Ltd
7 Battle Road
St Leonards-On-Sea, TN37 7AA
Tel: 01424 427393
Fax: 01424 717064
Promotes ways of living which seek, as far as possible and practical, to exclude all forms of exploitation of animals for food, clothing or any other purpose. In dietary terms, veganism entails dispensing with all forms of animal produce – including meat, fish and poultry. The society produces magazines, factsheets and a wide range of other literature. Ask for their publications list.

The Vegetarian Society of the United Kingdom Ltd
Parkdale
Dunham Road
Altrincham
Cheshire, WA14 4QG
Tel: 0161 928 0793
Produces a wide range of information. Their student resource pack *Vegetarian Issues* has sections on animal welfare, slaughter and transport.

VIVA
12 Queen Square
Brighton, BN1 3FD
Tel: 01273 777688
Fax: 01273 776755
Publishes 12 *Viva* Guides. They also have a new book published in September 1997: *The Livewire Guide to Going, Being and Staying Veggie* by Juliet Gellatley. Published by The Women's Press.

INDEX

The Internet has been likened to shopping in a supermarket without aisles. The press of a button on a Web browser can bring up thousands of sites but working your way through them to find what you want can involve long and frustrating on-line searches. And unfortunately many sites contain inaccurate, misleading or heavily biased information. Our researchers have therefore undertaken an extensive analysis to bring you a selection of quality Web site addresses. If our readers feel that this new innovation in the series is useful, we plan to provide a more extensive Web site section in each new book in the *Issues* series.

*****

Mimi's Cyber Kitchen
www.cyber-kitchen.com
Mimi's Cyber Kitchen is easy to use and comprehensive. It has more than 40 different categories, including information on vegetarian food, bread, cheese, health foods, food news groups, ethnic foods, plus recipes.

Ministry of Agriculture, Fisheries and Food (MAFF)
www.maff.gov.uk/maffhome.htm
Using animal welfare as a search term on this site produced 100 documents. Worth a look.

National Farmers' Union (NFU)
www.nfu.org.uk
The NFU aims to encourage a greater understanding of farming and rural life among school children and the wider public. Their site provides student and teacher resources.

The Vegan Society Ltd
www.vegansociety.com
A useful site for general information, publications, local contacts, travel information, product guides and links to other pages. Regularly updated.

The Vegetarian Society of the United Kingdom Ltd
www.vegsoc.org
There are separate sections for new veggies, youth pages, a food and drink index, recipes index, details of its Cordon Vert Cookery School and a local directory featuring good veggie places to eat, shop and stay in the UK and overseas.

VIVA
www.viva.org.uk
A lively and informative site: factsheets, campaigns, press releases, books etc.

WEBster Vegetarian Resources
www.katsden.com/webster/veg.html
The WEBster Vegetarian Resources is a good place to launch into veggie cyberspace. It has dozens of links into veggie, environmental and animal welfare sites and includes separate listing for general resources and recipes.

ACKNOWLEDGEMENTS

The publisher is grateful for permission to reproduce the following material.

While every care has been taken to trace and acknowledge copyright, the publisher tenders its apology for any accidental infringement or where copyright has proved untraceable. The publisher would be pleased to come to a suitable arrangement in any such case with the rightful owner.

Chapter One: A Question of Diet

The great veggie debate, © The Daily Mail, April 1998, *Meat in the diet*, © The British Nutrition Foundation, January 1998, *Big meat eaters cancer warning*, © The Daily Mail, September 1997, *Red meat consumption versus male colon cancer mortality*, © FAO Primary Livestock Data and World Health Organisation Health Statistics, 1990, *Fruit and two veg anyone?*, © The Guardian, September 1997, *Fruit and vegetable consumption per capita*, © FAO Crop Production Statistics, 1990, *50 per cent are eating less meat*, © Telegraph Group Limited, London 1997, *The Christian argument for vegetarianism*, © Rev. Dr Andrew Lindzey, Director of Studies, Centre for the Study of Theology, University of Essex, *Wear the shoes, eat the bacon sandwich*, © Liberator Publications, *Meat cheats fry in the face of being veggie*, © The Daily Mail, March 1998, *Breaking it gently*, © The Vegetarian Society, 1998, *Wot no beef?*, © The Vegetarian Society, 1998, *Pure murder?*, © The Guardian, March 1998, *Research reveals school confusion over vegetarianism*, © The Vegetarian Society, February 1998, *I'm sick of vegetarian hypocrisy*, © The Food Magazine, *Tricky questions, expert answers*, © The Vegetarian Society, 1998, *Being a veggie was murder*, © The Independent, December 1997, *Meat the facts*, © Tony Middlemiss, *Vegetarians are less likely to die of heart disease*, © Imperial Cancer Research Fund (ICRF), *Composition of expenditure on household food and drink*, © National Food Survey MAFF, 1997, *'A record 3 million vegetarians in the UK'*, © The Realeat Survey Office, *Myths about vegetarian food*, © Animal Aid, *13,000 people per week give up red meat!*, © The Realeat Survey Office, *Meat consumption*, © Meat and Livestock Commission (MLC).

Chapter Two: Ethical Concerns

Vegetarianism, © Animal Aid, January 1998, *The growth in non meat-eating*, © The Realeat Survey Office, *Wrecking the planet*, © Animal Aid, January 1998, *Free-range chickens and the hypocrisy of being vegetarian*, © The Daily Mail, October 1997, *Market share*, © Taylor Nelson AGB, *Factory farming*, © Animal Aid, *Animal Welfare*, © National Farmers' Union, *British chicken facts*, © The British Poultry Meat Federation Ltd, *Laying hens*, © Compassion in World Farming (CIWF), *Broiler chickens*, © Compassion in World Farming (CIWF), *Why go vegetarian?*, © The Vegetarian Society and Animal Aid, *The RSPCA's welfare standards for farm animals*, © RSPCA, *Why vegan?*, © Vegan Action, *Vegetarians and vegans, by sex*, © The Realeat Survey Office.

Photographs and illustrations:

Pages 1, 3, 11, 14, 32, 37: The Attic Publishing Co., pages 8, 10, 15, 19, 26: Ken Pyne, page 13: Andrew Smith.

Thank you

Darin Jewell for assisting in the editorial research for this publication.

Craig Donnellan
Cambridge
September, 1998